MIDWEST RESEARCH INSTITUTE

SOME RECOLLECTIONS OF THE FIRST 30 YEARS

MIDWEST RESEARCH INSTITUTE

SOME RECOLLECTIONS OF
THE FIRST 30 YEARS
1945 • 1975

CHARLES N. KIMBALL

PUBLISHED BY MIDWEST RESEARCH INSTITUTE

Funding for this history was provided by the Trustees
of Midwest Research Institute through a grant from the
Kimball Fund.

The author gratefully acknowledges the assistance of
Jane Mobley in the preparation of the text.

Book design by Orval Thrasher
Printed in Kansas City
by The Lowell Press, 1985

Library of Congress Catalog Card Number: 85-61137

CONTENTS

FOREWORD

by
Morton I. Sosland

This book is a history of the first 30 years of Midwest Research Institute. But it is also the mirror image of a man; and it is to him, his central role in the growth and evolution of the Institute, and his primacy as a leader of Kansas City and the Midwest that this foreword is directed. Charles Newton Kimball, President Emeritus of MRI and the active leader of that organization from 1950 to 1975, tells here in words and pictures the history of the Institute during the time he was at its helm. The book speaks persuasively for the Institute. I hope to do as well in his behalf.

My coming to this task reflects my position as chairman of MRI's Board of Trustees at the time Dr. Kimball initiated his retirement plans, recommended John McKelvey as his successor, and stepped aside at age 64. It was my special pleasure to preside over several retirement events honoring Dr. Kimball, to present him with the MRI Citation at the annual trustee dinner on May 15, 1975, and to lead the Board in naming the Institute's central building in his honor.

That the story did not begin in Kansas City, but in Boston, often surprises people who don't know his history and assume he has been a part of our city's fabric from time immemorial. Of English-Irish parentage with a firm background in New England, he was born April 21, 1911, in Boston, right on Bunker Hill. He grew up in a working-class neighborhood, and saved enough and worked enough to pay his way through Northeastern University, from which he received his undergraduate degree. He enrolled in graduate school at Harvard University, where he studied electrical engineering and from which he received the master's and doctorate degrees.

His first job was with RCA, which happily launched him on a career in what was then the relatively new field of telecommunications. He also became involved with electronics, including aircraft equipment, coming to Kansas City first in 1941 on assignments with several local companies. Even at a relatively young age, he caught the attention of the city's leadership; after he had left Kansas City to accept an executive research position with Bendix Aviation in Detroit, he received an urgent call to return and accept the presidency of Midwest Research Institute. This he did, in 1950, the sixth year of MRI and his 39th year.

From the perspective of those of us who served on the Board of Trustees of the Institute and especially on the Executive Committee, our position and his position were well defined. He never passed over to the Trustees the hard decisions or difficult actions required of the leader of an institution subject to the ebb and flow of the national economy. The task of each Trustee was to be an advocate of MRI, to be alert to research opportunities, to be aware of developments within one's own field that might influence the direction of the Institute's work. He was amazingly persuasive, and most of us came to look on him as our leader, even our teacher, in how best to run a nonprofit organization functioning for the general good. He showed us that a nonprofit organization could be run well, efficiently, and with verve, while effectively serving its primary public role.

Of course, some of us had the chance of getting to know him particularly well. Etched in my memory is his worrying about how the vote would go on a particular issue or project. Yet, he never lost one of those votes, largely as a result of his own adherence to his most frequently stated injunction: "Chance favors the prepared mind."

The Institute's history provides many instructive insights into the Kimball character. He has not been a visible fund-raiser in the sense of chairing grand campaigns. But he has been amazingly effective in coming up with ideas for raising funds. On several occasions, he has suggested to individuals that this or that project might be worthy of sponsorship. Most of the facilities that bear a family name at the Institute grew out of this targeted approach.

Dr. Kimball never had to go to the supporters of MRI for operating funds (and under his leadership MRI never had a deficit — a unique accomplishment for a nonprofit organization in the volatile research field). It was the absence of general fund-raising by MRI, due in large part to his prudent management, that in 1970 led the Executive Committee to create the Kimball Fund, a fund contributed mainly by a corpus of companies and individuals who admire both the man and the institution.

The only exception to his aversion to mass fund-raising arose when he took on the task, as a personal crusade, of saving and expanding Science Pioneers. He annually for over 20 years wrote personal letters to hundreds of friends and succeeded in securing the necessary funding. As a result, Science Pioneers in Kansas City, which annually sponsors the Greater Kansas City Science and Engineering Fair for high school students and a series of lectures as well, has become the most successful of such endeavors across the country.

While MRI has been the central focus of Kimball's business life, he also has had an important and impressive career outside the Institute. Two corporate boards have been especially important to him — Hallmark Cards, Inc., Kansas City's preeminent corporation, on whose board he served from 1962 to 1976, and Trans World Airlines and Trans World Corporation, where he was a board member from 1965 to 1981.

In the public arena, Dr. Kimball's labors have been prodigious, especially for someone who himself was at the helm of a nonprofit organization. To list all these activities would make for an unwieldy catalogue. Several stand out, though. While still active as President of MRI, he and Donald J. Hall, President of Hallmark Cards, Inc., headed the Prime Time program that catapulted Kansas City into national prominence.

In what might be called the philanthropic field, the Kimball contributions are astounding. They range all the way from chairing the United Way and then pitching in to reshape that organization's direction, to leading in the establishment of two organizations of tremendous importance to our community's future. He has been a leader in the Clearinghouse for Midcontinent Foundations from its start in 1975, and was the first chairman and truly the "father" of the Greater Kansas City Community Foundation, established in 1979, which had the best starting record of any similar community foundation in the United States.

Dr. Kimball now actively supports the Mid America Heart Institute at St. Luke's Hospital. He is also a guiding force behind the St. Luke's Foundation after serving on the hospital's board for a number of years. He has been a trustee of the Kansas City Art Institute for many years, and has had an active role in the Society of Fellows at the Nelson-Atkins Museum of Art.

He has been the recipient of practically every civic honor that counts in Kansas City, and he also has several honorary degrees to his credit. It is axiomatic that his fellow Kansas Citians have come to look to him to provide guidance and advice in almost every major civic undertaking, but his outside activities on the national scene are also important. He was an early participant in the Young Presidents' Organization, actually being the first YPO member in Kansas City, and he also worked closely with the Committee for Economic Development. Since 1977, he has served on the Advisory Committee to the Office of Technology Assessment, a research arm of the Congress, and he was chairman of this prestigious committee for four years.

For many years, Dr. Kimball has been a watercolorist, maintaining a studio at home. His watercolors have been displayed in public spaces on a number of occasions and are in demand from those who know his talents.

His greatest post-retirement interest, though, has become genealogy and family history. His first completed work related the story of the family of Mary Louise Theis Kimball, his wife. In his own family's genealogy, he has researched the histories of the six generations of Kimballs and Rileys (his mother's name) who have lived in the greater Boston area, and he has become closely affiliated with the New England Historic Genealogical Society. He also has been instrumental in securing for the University of Missouri at Kansas City's Western Historical Manuscript collection the historical records of a number of prominent local citizens, including his own.

Preparing this foreword to the history of MRI written by Dr. Kimball has given me reason again to think about him as a man, as a citizen of this region and country, as a friend, and as a leader. His has been, and continues to be, an amazingly productive life. The reader of this book will quickly appreciate how Kimball has shaped MRI, affirming as much as anyone the wisdom of another Bostonian, Ralph Waldo Emerson, who said, "An institution is the lengthened shadow of a man."

Charles Kimball moved MRI while at its helm; he continues to move the community in which he lives, and he sets a course that makes all who know him much the better for it.

Morton T. Seelord.

AUTHOR'S NOTE

This is an informal history. Its genesis was in conversation, in the inevitable reminiscences that come from long association with a vital and fascinating organization. It has taken a long time to produce because for years I felt I was too close to the past to see it retrospectively.

Gradually, however, I began to see the events of Midwest Research Institute's first three decades in patterns that could be explained. And perhaps more importantly, I began to see the people of MRI's past connected to the people of MRI's future by forces that needed to be described if they were to be understood. Institutions are like families: every generation has its own challenges and struggles, but there is much to be learned from knowing about previous generations' triumphs and failures. When the memories of the early days are lost, something rich and precious is lost too. That is sad, and it is also dangerous, because institutions — like families — who forget where they have come from are less able to understand where they are going.

The values of an organization are established in the early years. Certainly, these values can and should change as the organization grows, but recognizing the role the early values played in the organization's history keeps change in the right perspective. A company or an institution — like a family — can find renewed inspiration in the dreams of its founders.

I am grateful to Trustees Donald Hall, Morton Sosland, Irvine Hockaday, and Robert Long who first suggested that there ought to be a written history of Midwest Research Institute. Listening to my anecdotes about MRI in the "old days," each of them at different times pressed for a written account.

That account would never have been put to paper had it not been for two individuals in particular: Martin Schuler, now Corporate Secretary of MRI, who has been at MRI since the very beginning; and Dr. Harold Orel, Distinguished Professor, Department of English, University of Kansas, who has served MRI since 1958 as a consultant on the writing of presentations.

This unique team of interviewers, steeped in the lore and substance of MRI, engaged me in the lengthy, taped oral sessions of remembrance that became the first version of this history.

Martin Schuler's recall is better than mine, and without his help many of the projects and people of years ago would not have been so readily identified in the pictures included here, and in the text. In many ways, this is the history of the life work of a group of people who deserve to have it told. Martin exemplifies those people in his contributions to MRI.

Harold Orel shaped the taped sessions, along with an enormous amount of his own research, into the initial drafts. Martin and Harold were more than mere historians for this volume; they've lived this history too.

This manuscript was written in its final form by Jane Mobley, a professional author and editor, who served also as the coordinator of the entire project, pictures and all, bringing this extensive history together as you now see it.

This history recounts scores of project undertakings involving a large number of competent professionals, but it was the singular combination of this staff and our Board of Trustees that made MRI such an unusual enterprise. Special thanks belong to those who have served as Chairman. J.C. Nichols, the first Chairman of the Trustees, died the year before I came, but with this one exception, I met with each of the Chairmen scores of times in their two years of service. Their sense of caring, concern, and active involvement are unmatched elsewhere in my own extensive institutional experience.

Of the Trustees and professional staff it may be said that their tenacity of purpose and their generosity of time and spirit remain an inspiring reminder of our early period of discovery. To these two groups this history is dedicated.

Charles N. Kimball

July 1985

THE
EARLY
YEARS

FOUNDING A
FREESTANDING INSTITUTE

Midwest Research Institute came about as one of those rare but wonderful phenomena that happen sometimes in the history of human problem solving: it was an answer that grew too big for its question. Out of the initial need of this area of the country to attract war contracts to bolster its economy sprang the idea that was to become Midwest Research Institute. A number of those contracts were indeed gained, but World War II was soon over and then the idea of centralizing some of the best of scientific inquiry in the region began to flower. Soon the institution that was meant as an answer was asking questions and creating demands on its own, and an exciting dynamic was building between the scientific resource and the community it was meant to serve. The community itself began growing, encouraged in part by the connections the Institute provided to science, technology, and the future. Along the way were new questions, new answers, and still newer questions in an unfolding dimension that the original founders of the Institute could scarcely have imagined.

Kansas City in 1940 was a pretty, pastoral town — not really the cowtown of so many jokes and stories, but certainly a community with a strong tie to agriculture. The broad boulevards and the relatively low rise of downtown buildings along with the sweeping fields lying in every direction away from the city gave a peaceful impression. This was no smokestack town, and when it became evident that the United States was going to be involved in another world war, community leaders were justifiably concerned that all war contracts would go to other parts of the country. They hoped to encourage Kansas City's participation in the war effort with factories that manufactured electronic equipment, aviation parts, and armaments. They believed that the region had reached a stage of development when agriculture could be balanced by industry.

But that point of view was not shared nationally. There were skeptical and powerful people in Washington who believed Kansas City to be not much more than a big farming community, and who found it very difficult to identify specific scientific and technological resources in the region.

They were not altogether mistaken. During the early 1940's, only about 500 chemists, engineers, and economists were working in the Kansas City area, most of them in small groups. As the war went on it became clear that, in the Midwest, a sensible pattern of growth in science should not be postponed until some future emergency again focused attention on technology. Moreover, a backed-up demand for technological goods and services seemed bound to spill over once the war was over, and the scientific expertise in Kansas City would not be able to satisfy such a need.

The city had another problem at the time that affected more than technology. The outmigration of the entire region had become alarming by the mid-1940's. Population statistics showed that more than 10 percent of the population was leaving every five years, going to more highly developed opportunities on the East and West Coasts. It was a haunting repeat of the Dust Bowl years of the early 1930's, but this time the migrants were not all farmers — in every arena some of the best talent was moving away.

Recruiting scientific staff to Kansas City was difficult until an effort was made to do it on a systematic and patriotic basis. War contracts and the promise of increased postwar technological production might do it, some leaders believed, if the area could be made a center for scientific activity.

In 1940, J. C. Nichols and Robert Mehornay went to Washington to accept dollar-a-year posts with the National Defense Advisory Council. Nichols was to have an important role in procurement of equipment for the armed forces and Mehornay to serve as director of small business activities. Both positions offered the men experience in handling defense contracts and increased their interest in bringing defense-related industry to the Midwest to bolster the region's economy.

They came to understand that after the war many scientists who had contributed to the war effort, as well as former members of the armed forces, would be looking for jobs; many of them would want to return to places they knew and loved from childhood. But the Midwest had few jobs to support them. These economic factors and the population patterns of the region were uppermost in the minds of the three men who set out to change Washington's mind about Kansas City. J. C. Nichols, as one of the foremost developers of planned residential communities in the United States, had a strong interest in population development and the general economic growth of Kansas City. His Country Club Plaza was the first regional outlying shopping center in the country. Robert L. Mehornay was a national spokesman for the furniture industry. Kenneth A. Spencer, of Pittsburg, Kansas, a town about 150 miles south of Kansas City, was vice president of his father's Pittsburg and Midway Coal Company, and he planned to develop a companion chemical business.

Meanwhile, Kenneth Spencer needed a chemical production contract from Washington to begin a diversified chemical production firm. He knew Kansas and Missouri had untapped resources — not just in the coal and petroleum that were there, but also in the trained technical people who had left homes in the Midwest but might well be lured back.

One story about Spencer's campaign to get this done illustrates the spirit of many of the negotiations that went on in the formative days of MRI. At a meeting of the site committee of the Advisory Council, Spencer had made a proposal for his chemical plants and an Eastern businessman commented, "That's all very well, except for one thing: you don't have the technical know-how in the West."

Spencer looked around the room. Every scientist there, including Dr. Ernest W. Reid, former head of research for Union Carbide Corporation, and Dr. Edward R. Weidlein, director of the Mellon Institute, had Kansas backgrounds. Spencer turned to the businessman. "This technical talent is Kansas talent. Everyone here is accounted for except for you and me. I don't know where you come from, but I come from Kansas."

He got his contract.

During the war, as his production plants spread out, Spencer had moved to Kansas City; and when Nichols and Mehornay were trying to raise interest in the development of the idea that would become MRI, they came to him.

By 1943, when the selection of war production facilities and contractors was complete, Kansas City had a number of them. Nichols was concerned that after the war the new plants would close and the impetus to the area's economy would be lost. He and other leaders believed that a research organization would help retain what had been gained, and would attract new industries to utilize the resources of the region.

This concept would never have gotten anywhere if those who supplied the initial investments had not had great faith in the credibility of the founders. In addition to the

15

original three men, there were some who were in technical fields: Dr. Roy Cross, president of the Kansas City Testing Laboratory; C. J. Patterson, a cereal chemist and president of the research company of Campbell-Taggart Baking, the company that would turn Holsum Bread into a household word of the 1950's; Charles T. Thompson, head of Thompson-Hayward Chemical Company; and J. F. Stephens, a mechanical engineer and vice president of the Gustin-Bacon Manufacturing Company, the sponsor of much MRI research in the years following.

Another of the founders, grain dealer Paul D. Bartlett, was the nephew of Herbert F. Hall, also a grain dealer, who had left an estate of more than $6 million to build a library in his wife's memory. The trust did not specify the library's emphasis, and initially Shakespearean material was favored as the centerpiece of the library's collections. Nichols and Mehornay met repeatedly with the trustees of the Linda Hall Library Trust and its chairman, Bartlett. Con-

vinced of the need for a technological resource in the Midwest, the trustees decided the Linda Hall collection would focus on scientific holdings. This was a critical development toward beginning a research institute. It is fair to say that without this library MRI could not have flourished as it has.

Initially, no one thought of developing an independent institute. The original plan called for coordinating research activities at major universities in the six-state area of Missouri, Kansas, Iowa, Nebraska, Arkansas, and Oklahoma. College researchers in chemistry, physics, biology, agronomy, and engineering would take on research projects requested and financed by business and industry, with a coordinating council to assign projects in the expanded use of regional resources. Called "The Midwest Research Council," the idea suited businessmen but not the universities. Inter-institutional rivalries created problems, and some university personnel were unwilling to pursue applied research toward the regional in-

President Harold Vagtborg (left, center) shows MRI Trustees a fiberglass project at the first annual meeting.

dustrial conversion the founders envisioned. Nor did they want to give up their own traditional rights to the patents or new processes developed from pure research.

Dr. Roy Cross probably first crystallized the idea of an independent institute. He knew about commercial laboratories and had made a success of his own in Kansas City. These laboratories did work for money, on contract, and he knew the bookkeeping and financing arrangements needed for such organizations. He was a persuasive champion of the idea that even a nonprofit institute must support itself.

The concept of a scientific research institute is not very old in American history. The Mellon Institute, for example, started in the decade after 1910, and the Armour Research Foundation in the early 1930's. The Battelle Institute was founded in the late 1920's as the fulfillment of Gordon Battelle's bequest of his estate. All three of these research institutes were visited by MRI's founders in the summer of 1943 when they realized their initial university-based plan couldn't succeed.

The Mellon Institute in Pittsburgh, Pennsylvania, the oldest and most solidly established of the three, was funded through the support of one family and depended on the prestigious Mellon Fellowships offered only to the best researchers and oriented toward independent research. This was not what MRI's founders wanted for Kansas City, so they went on to Columbus, Ohio, to the Battelle Memorial Institute. Battelle had pioneered the practice of contract research in which a sponsor defined the project and paid the bill for the costs of technical personnel and equipment, as well as an amount for administrative overhead. Upon completion of the project, the sponsor received all reports and patents along with the assurance that the work had been done exclusively for him.

Then the group visited the Armour Research Foundation in Chicago, which operated similarly to Battelle. There they met the president, Dr. Harold Vagtborg, who offered to be of any help that he could. Eventually he was named the first president of MRI.

Back home, Cross, Patterson, Nichols, Mehornay, and Spencer settled on a plan to develop an independent, not-for-profit research institute that would perform scientific research for sponsors. Rather than seek long-term sponsorship, the Institute would perform the research as needs came along; once a project was finished, its sponsor would choose whether or not to bring another problem to the Institute for a solution. The Institute would also serve as a clearinghouse for scientific information to be shared with the community, and as a focal point of technical assistance to large and small industrial and agricultural interests.

On December 7, 1943, nine men signed a request for incorporation of the Midwest Research Institute with the Jackson County Circuit Court. Nichols, Mehornay, and Spencer signed first. Then Cross and Patterson signed, both of whom would serve on the initial scientific advisory board of the new Institute. Bartlett was the sixth incorporator, followed by Benjamin C. Adams, chief executive officer for the Gas Service Company and a civil engineer, then by Charles T. Thompson and J. F. Stephens.

The charter was unusual in its emphasis on regional development through science, a new direction for research institutes. The founders were more than hometown boosters. They believed in the Midwest's potentially dynamic mix of industry, resource utilization, and food, fiber, and livestock production and processing. They wanted to turn an area of the country that was all but ignored, except for its natural resources, into a self-supporting region.

In addition to scientific discovery, which quickly became the daily work of the Institute, there was the ongoing revelation of limitless resources of imagination and skill, and of community needs and opportunities hardly foretold at the time of the Institute's founding. For MRI and for the Midwest it was the beginning of an era of discovery.

THE PERIOD OF DISCOVERY

By the summer of 1944, the newly chartered Midwest Research Institute had a staff, was housed in borrowed and rented buildings, and had begun its first successful fund-raising drive. Dr. W. T. Rinehart, on leave from the Armour Research Foundation, was Acting Director, hired on the recommendation of Dr. Harold Vagtborg, president of Armour Research Foundation and an advisor to the Board of Trustees of MRI. In November 1944, Vagtborg himself became the first Director and President of MRI.

In his early role as advisor to the Trustees, Vagtborg had assisted with the fund raising that began almost immediately after the charter was signed. In April, three months before the Institute officially opened for business, more than 130 area businessmen met to hear Vagtborg describe the success of Armour Research Foundation and reveal that the call for research was growing so fast that Armour had turned down more than $2 million in available contracts in the previous six months. There was more than enough research to be done, he said, just not enough organizations to do it. The goal for MRI's initial development fund was set at $500,000 to be paid over four years until MRI could support itself on contracts. By opening day, over half the $500,000 goal had been subscribed by 42 businesses and individuals in gifts ranging from $1,500 to $30,000.

In these months of preparation, the first of the Institute's homes was a building owned by C. J. Patterson's Campbell-Taggart Research Corporation. Staffing was a troublesome challenge since most qualified technicians and scientists were still in military service or engaged in war-related projects. Women with enough ad-

vanced experience or graduate training to head research projects were rare at that time. Acting Director Rinehart hired as project directors a few men who were not in military service because they had been teachers or students of subjects considered essential to the war effort. For example, Martin Schuler had just received his degree in biology from the University of Kansas City, and was hired as the first full-time technical employee of the Institute.

In 1944 and early 1945, projects came in more rapidly than staff could be hired to research them. MRI had to maintain a waiting list of potential sponsors. The impressive list included local firms such as the Gas Service Company, Gustin-Bacon Manufacturing, Spencer Chemical Company, and the Kansas City Testing Laboratory, as well as regional firms such as Phillips Petroleum and the W. J. Small (later Airosol) Company, and national sponsors such as the Carnation Company and the Chicago Bridge and Iron Company. As Vagtborg had promised the initial supporters, the demand was certainly there.

Once Vagtborg was named Director and President, he set about hiring personnel to head research areas. Because of a growing staff and project roster, the Institute was getting too big for the space rented from Campbell-Taggart and too busy to make do much longer with equipment borrowed from the bakery's research organization. To solve the space problem, Vagtborg acquired the old Westport City Hall at the southeast corner of 40th Street Terrace and Pennsylvania Avenue. It had been built in 1886 as a fire and police station. When Vagtborg arranged for use of an adjoining building, the Midwest Research Institute was settled squarely on Westport Road, a remnant of the historic Santa Fe Trail. Aptly, it was the very spot that had served as an outfitters' center for another kind of pioneering spirit only three generations before.

The first months at MRI were arduous indeed. Staff had to be recruited, equipment bought, contracts secured. Technical staff were often burdened with administrative duties instead of being able to do the research for which they had been hired. Procedures were sometimes more cumbersome than necessary. For example, the Trustees required double signatures on checks, and Martin Schuler recalls taking all prepared payroll checks downtown to the office of Ben Adams, the first MRI Treasurer, then catching the trolley back to the Plaza office of J. C. Nichols, then Chairman of the Board of Trustees, before returning to Westport to distribute the checks. Within months, Adams selected Leon T. Swan to become Assistant Treasurer. A young homebuilder with a strong business talent, Swan soon streamlined MRI operations. He provided efficiency and stability to MRI's business operations for 25 years, and eventually became Senior Vice President and Chief Financial Officer.

During these early years, another person critical to MRI's development was hired to come to Kansas City, although not to the Institute itself. In late 1945, Joseph C. Shipman moved from the Enoch Pratt Library in Baltimore to

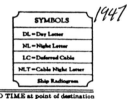

1947

CLASS OF SERVICE		SYMBOLS	
This is a full-rate Telegram or Cablegram unless its deferred character is indicated by a suitable symbol above or preceding the address.		DL = Day Letter	
		NL = Night Letter	
		LC = Deferred Cable	
		NLT = Cable Night Letter	
		Ship Radiogram	

The filing time sh A867   line on telegrams and day letters is STANDARD TIME at point of origin. Time of receipt is STANDARD TIME at point of destination

A.WA210 NL GOVT PD=THE WHITE HOUSE WASHINGTON DC 7   1947 DEC 7 PM 8 01

ROBERT L MEHORNAY CHAIRMAN=

    BOARD OF GOVER NORS MIDWEST RESEARCH INSTITUTE HOTEL

    MUEHLEBACH KSC=

THERE MUST BE NO RETROGRESSION IN THE MARCH **FORWARD OF THE**
MIDWEST RESEARCH INSTITUTE IN ITS DETERMINATION **TO DEVELOP**
THE RESOURCES OF THE MIDWESTERN STATES. GREAT AS OUR WEALTH
BOTH GRICULTURE AND MINERALS WE NEED TO DEVELOP THOSE
RESOURCES THROUGH EXPANDING INDUSTRIES. ONLY THEN **SHALL WE**

ACHIEVE A BALANCED ECONOMY. ONLY THEN SHALL **WE** BRING GREATER
PROSPERITY, HAPPINESS AND SECURITY TO ALL OF THE PEOPLE OF
THE RICH MIDWEST. MY MESSAGE TO THE THIRD ANNUAL MEETING OF
THE BOARD OF TRUSTEES, OF WHICH I AM PROUD TO BE A MEMBER IS
TO GO FORWARD WITH PROGRESS UNTIL MID-AMERICA IS IN A
POSITION TO MAKE TO THE NATIONAL ECONOMY THE FULL
CONTRIBUTION OF WHICH SHE IS CAPABLE. MY HEARTY
FELICITATIONS AND WARMEST PERSONAL GREETINGS TO ALL WHO
ATTEND THE MEETING TODAY=

    HARRY S TRUMAN.

become head librarian at the Linda Hall Library of Science and Technology. Paul Bartlett, one of the nine original incorporators of MRI, also headed the Linda Hall Board of Trustees, and he guided Shipman's initial assignment — to assemble a true science library — in a direction that was crucial to the Institute's own growth and success. Shipman's development of scientific holdings for the library was aided by MRI scientists who would be major users of the materials.

At this time, the Institute was trying to fashion its various parts into a working whole. Staff, location, resources, and administration began to find productive arrangements; contracts were negotiated and the direction that the Institute would take in the future with its sponsors was worked out in practice during early projects. The principle underlying all this activity was clear from the outset. MRI had been charged with a dual goal: to supply needed research on a contract basis for industry, and to encourage the development of research programs to utilize regional resources. But the first contracts raised questions and problems that could not have been imagined until the Institute began to replace hopes with real projects.

In the beginning, MRI's staff suggested projects they believed would benefit the region. For example, the Institute began with the notion that there were vast underdeveloped resources on all sides. Looking back, it is now possible to see that this was not altogether true — at least not as MRI had originally thought. Certainly, vast deposits of clay and metals did exist, but the companies that exploited them were developing their own technology and did not need to buy scientific research through a research institute. One of the early staff proposals was for a project to find new ceramic and refractory clays for improving firebrick. As it turned out, commercial companies already knew where the clays were located and what potential uses for them existed.

In some cases, a need for a project existed but the Institute staff simply couldn't find suitable results. For example, there were proposals to find uses of vegetable fiber otherwise discarded in processing, and to develop an inexpensive surface for cattle feedlots. The vegetable fibers proposed as substitutes for hemp in the making of cordage products proved to be too limited in commercial use. A plan for reducing mud in cattle feedlots turned out to be prohibitively expensive; even today, most feedlots are muddy.

Clearly, generating projects internally was not working, and the relationship of MRI to its project sponsors began to take shape. It appeared that the Institute would do well to provide assistance to small companies that lacked technology or equipment. From the beginning, the Institute underwrote the cost of buying basic equipment, recruiting personnel, and establishing appropriate quarters. It organized and established the operations of various projects in a practical way. But only when the Institute made the decision to work on the problems of the sponsor rather than follow its own ideas as to where problems lay, did it start being successful.

Today that approach seems obvious, but when the concept of contract research was new, neither researchers nor sponsors fully understood how different it was from academic research. An important difference, which MRI learned from experience, now is axiomatic in the research business and has to do with working directly with sponsors. Dr. Russell W. Dayton, an executive of Battelle Memorial Institute, has summed it up effectively: "Unlike fundamental research, contract research cannot be done by scientists working alone and communicating only with their peers. . .Researchers must communicate often and well with the world of applied science — especially their sponsors. Excellence has a completely different meaning for contract than for academic research. Contract research is satisfying a sponsor's real needs most completely — or demonstrating that these needs cannot be satisfied — in the shortest time and for a suitable expenditure."

One of the biggest challenges at the very beginning was making the potential of the Institute known. Many companies did not understand how best to utilize the expertise and facilities MRI offered; chief executive officers at that time often did not know what science and technology could do for them. Some of the companies were concerned about keeping the proprietary secrets of their industrial processes and did not want to share these secrets with a research institute. Actually, all contracts the Institute signed with sponsors stipulated that the rights for research-developed technology belonged exclusively to the sponsor.

A greater obstacle than secrecy lay in simple ignorance. Many companies did not know what a research institute could do. They worried that their investment would not be worthwhile and that they might be merely underwriting the expenses of a thesis or dissertation supervised by a professional with no real interest in the applied results of the project. They worried that they might not be getting first-class research; there had been enough inadequately scaled projects and incomplete or slightly sour results from research institutes in the 1930's and early 1940's that the business community shared an understandable suspicion.

Moreover, educational institutions in the Midwest were not altogether sure of the role the Institute intended to play, and universities sometimes regarded it as a competitor. Some chancellors and presidents of universities wrote letters to J. C. Nichols, complaining that the founding of the Institute represented a threat to the flow of work that they would normally receive from government and industry. Soon, however, the objections to MRI began to diminish, and in time virtually every college president of a major institution in the region became a Trustee of MRI. By 1959, many of them were serving as Trustees, and educational institutions were important allies with MRI in the work of expanding technological resources in the Midwest.

Ultimately, the Trustees and MRI professional leadership came to understand that sponsored projects with a closely defined goal, and access to the sponsor's records of all previous research into that particular problem, were the best route to successful research. Once the scientists learned to settle with the sponsor what the problems really were, and to draw up a proposal for attacking them for a specific sum of money, the Institute had a project policy grounded in practice and the contract arrangement began to succeed.

Although every project has been important to the history of MRI, the early projects were crucial. The ones that didn't yield the anticipated results could not be called failures; they were important elements of the defining and focusing process the Institute was undergoing. The successful projects also contributed to this process, and they, of course, were the ones on which MRI's reputation began to build.

As its first project, the Institute undertook an ammonium nitrate water absorption problem encountered by the Spencer Chemical Company. In many ways that first research problem exemplified what MRI had been organized to investigate. If it succeeded, the research would develop a useful product whose manufacture could keep a factory in continued production. The problem the researchers faced was the long-recognized property of ammonium nitrate that caused clumping. When the compound absorbed water, it caked and became unusable. Even transporting it was a problem. Ships bringing natural nitrate compounds to the United States often had to have the cargo broken out of the hold with pickaxes. To be used as an agricultural fertilizer, ammonium nitrate had to be made available as a product that was free-flowing in small granules.

MRI scientists searching for answers to the ammonium nitrate problem were able to use the new collection being developed by the Linda Hall Library. This first project revealed the immeasurable value the growing library holdings would have for MRI.

The clumping problem was eventually solved. After the chance remark of a staff member not regularly assigned to the project, the nitrate crystals were examined under a geologist's petrographic microscope — borrowed from a nearby university. Indeed, the microscopic examination showed the crystals to be full of minute, water-retaining pockets. Nearly a year and a half after the project started, MRI chemists discovered a compound that would dust the crystals, sealing the pockets and lubricating the crystals to assure that they remained separate when poured from bags as commercial fertilizer.

With the patent to the new process, the Spencer Chemical Company was able not only to convert existing factories in Kansas and Missouri to peacetime use, but also to build new plants to keep up with the demand for the highly usable fertilizer. The end of MRI's first contract research project was more than a chemical compound; it was the creation of new jobs within the Institute's primary service area.

Much of the early work of MRI emphasized chemistry. Another successful project of this period was a contract with the J. A. Folger Company, which had a coffee production plant in Kansas City, to make a palatable instant coffee (the early instant coffee available during the war had been foul-tasting). MRI scientists developed a palatable product, then built an experimental plant in the basement of the old Westport fire station to show how the new substance could be produced.

Interestingly, one early program was begun because Western Cartridge had been approached by prominent duck hunters. They were concerned about the number of ducks poisoned by lead shot discharged by hunters over lakes and then eaten by the ducks. Western Cartridge wanted to manufacture iron shot that would not be poisonous. Shot had previously been made round by the costly and time-consuming process of dropping bits of lead from a shot tower several

hundred feet high; by the time the molten lead reached the bottom it was round and hardened. MRI set up a system of making shot in a tower only a foot high, with a rotating screen to round the molten iron as it went through. It was an ingenious invention, and it made a contribution to conservation long before the term became fashionable.

As word of these kinds of successes began to spread, other challenging projects came to the Institute that were suitable to the talents gathered there. MRI was fortunate from the very beginning to have Trustees who were eager to publicize the activities and the local presence of MRI. The *Kansas City Star* assigned reporters to follow newsworthy activities at the Institute. Few area institutions attracted as much regional attention as MRI did in its first 20 years.

The Trustees also helped through contributions, sometimes through advocacy, and by regarding their appointment as an honor worth talking about with other business leaders in the region. In these ways, MRI began to be known and was on its way toward fulfilling the goal of its founders to bring to the Midwest the scientific skills needed for industry to prosper.

Already in 1947, the Westport space was too small, and J. C. Nichols negotiated a purchase for $37,500 of a 10-acre tract of land adjacent to the University of Kansas City campus, within a block of the Linda Hall Library. At the end of the wide sweep of lawn leading down from the William Rockhill Nelson Gallery, and close to the burgeoning Country Club Plaza, the site was at the heart of Kansas City's cultural and intellectual growth.

But plans for the new building were set aside in 1948 when Harold Vagtborg, first President of MRI, resigned. He had accepted the presidency of Southwest Research Institute in San Antonio, Texas. It was the end of MRI's embarkation. The change in leadership signaled a new phase for the Institute, which would grow into maturity in the next decade.

NEW BUSINESS, NEW BUILDINGS, NEW DIRECTIONS

After Harold Vagtborg left, the Institute was run for a brief time by a committee. Dr. George E. Ziegler, who had earlier been at the Armour Research Foundation, was in charge of research, and Robert Mehornay was President, primarily in charge of development. This splitting of scientific and administrative fund-raising responsibilities was not really successful. Such matters as daily receipts and cash flow became the topic of interminable discussions in the Executive Committee, and with the Board of Governors, as they tried to work out problems of location, staffing, and project funding. Soon the Trustees began to look for someone who might serve the Institute in the dual capacity of businessman and scientist.

When Mehornay, Patterson, and Spencer called to invite me to interview for the presidency of MRI, I was the technical director of Bendix Aviation Corporation Central Research Laboratories. Before going to Detroit in that capacity, I had worked in Kansas City as vice president of the Aircraft Accessories Corporation. It was during these years between 1941 and 1948 that I had gotten acquainted with C. J. Patterson. Although my career at Bendix was promising, the challenge of MRI was irresistible. I came back to Kansas City in June 1950 to become President of the Institute.

In the early days that was a jack-of-all-trades type of job. Just as our then scientific methods seem primitive by today's standards, so must our old administrative ways. I helped get buildings put up, made speeches, got Trustees involved, spent some time in the laboratories with clients, and tried out new pieces of equipment. But from the start I saw the job of the President as being an enabling force for the staff. Neither management nor scientific personnel can make intelligent decisions about a client's projects without each other's help. The growth of the Institute in its early years can be attributed to a constant, successful sharing and caring for each other throughout MRI at every level.

A formidable task at the beginning of my time with MRI was publicity; the Institute needed to become more widely known. Our local publicity had always been good, thanks to the efforts of many local supporters. But the Institute had to be nationally known if it was to serve its stated purpose. I began to travel, making speeches at the rate of about 100 a year. My theme was always that technology was necessary to the future of the Midwest. Gradually, the Trustees saw the value of marketing, and economic research as well, and the scope of MRI broadened accordingly. So did the subject matter of all those speaking engagements as MRI's growth provided more information to share.

As the staff grew, the reputation of MRI grew with it. Once, a soybean company in Illinois called the Institute because the president of the company had heard that Dr. Max Thornton, who became MRI's Vice President and Technical Director, was working at MRI. The president of the soybean company responded to a question about how he had heard of MRI by saying that any place employing Max H. Thornton had to be good. Through personal testaments such as this, and through a variety of other means — including, for a short time, use of a public relations agency in New York — MRI began to gain national visibility.

In the beginning, the issue was raised whether we could accept any work from outside the six-state area. The proposal in question was a research program for a company that operated in Illinois across the Mississippi River from St. Louis! Before too many years had passed, MRI was welcoming projects from clients who needed the Institute's services, no matter where those clients were based.

One of the Institute's standards for self-assessment has always been what might be called "client outcome." Did the client or sponsor of a project get what was needed? MRI was never intended to be an organization dedicated to pure research; its applied research has always been sponsor-based, and keeping that sponsor satisfied is crucial to any project. Probably because this approach is integral to MRI's philosophy, most of the Institute's projects over the years have been "repeat business," clients who come back with more projects because they are pleased.

At first the biggest problem with sponsors was getting them to say what they needed, to define their own programs. A proverb we had in those days was, "The tougher the sponsor, the better the job we do." When a sponsor knew what was wanted, MRI could usually supply it.

We assured hesitant sponsors that MRI was trustworthy; indeed, privacy never was a problem. Sponsors acquired all the rights to a process or a product, and, furthermore, if MRI needed to develop a process or product in its own laboratories at the Institute, the client was allowed to send people to visit the Institute for training to help smooth the transition to their own in-house research. In certain instances, a client's employees worked on a loan basis in MRI's laboratories, then went back to the home company with the new knowledge or skills they needed.

Contract research was new to many companies in those days. Sometimes, after they had bought the necessary research, they didn't do anything with it. In the light of today's sophisticated marketing techniques for even the smallest companies, it seems almost unbelievable that part of MRI's task was to urge sponsors to use a little project money for a market survey before they entered into a research contract so they could have some idea of where the new product or process might go. This nudging was the beginning of MRI's Economics Division. Trade associations helped a great deal in teaching companies how to use contract research. For example, when MRI did a project for the Manufacturing Chemists Association or the National Renderers Association, cooperative programs with defined goals were written and member firms began to participate in these. From this involvement, they learned how contract research was done. Some of them eventually became clients of MRI on their own.

As public awareness of the Institute was growing, so were the demands placed on it. Flexibility became a byword at MRI. A contract research institute moves with the needs for research. It enters research areas, performs the work, and moves on with opportunity.

Even though most of MRI's early projects emphasized chemistry, the Institute has tried not to confine itself to only one corner of the scientific world or one kind of problem. At MRI, sections change and new divisions are formed as new needs and new professional skills come into existence. Long-time employees at MRI steadily redefine their competence, expanding their interests and skills as new projects come in. Scientists have to change with new patterns and new ideas or they stagnate, and do not get new business — which for a research institute is the same as withering on the vine.

New business did come to MRI; proposal requests began to come in from both the private and public sectors. After the surge of war research and postwar conversion projects passed, gains in research volume were moderate, only 8 to 10 percent. Then, in the first fiscal year after 1950, the gain was 44 percent.

The first government project was brought into the Institute by Martin Goland, a young Cornell engineering graduate whose earlier work in mechanical engineering had attracted some attention in Washington. At that time the government was not really a frequent buyer of research from organizations such as MRI. However, through Goland's efforts and reputation, MRI began to get some federal projects. This research concentrated on aircraft stability and design vibrations, high frequency electronics, and the recoilless rifle.

The variety of contracts MRI received during the 1950's was amazing; in a short time, the Institute had come a long way from its war-related genesis. From ballistics to bananas, it was to be an exciting decade of research for everyone concerned.

MRI's scientists and technicians needed to be experts on the project under assignment. In some cases, that meant starting from the ground up, as it did for a project sponsored by the Standard Fruit and Steamship Company of New Orleans, which owned huge banana plantations at La Ceiba in the Republic of Honduras, Central America. Crops were suffering "tip-over"; just before the banana stems were ripe enough to be cut and shipped to the United States, the stems weakened and toppled over. The individual bananas, five to six dozen per stem, were then unsalvageable because of bruising or because they could not mature properly. In some sections of the plantations, up to 30 percent of the stems were affected by tip-over and Standard's own staff was stymied.

MRI scientists assigned to solve this problem first learned everything they could about bananas and concluded that tip-over was probably caused by a microorganism. When the researchers began their surveys of the plantations, they had to take all the necessary

paraphernalia with them to Honduras because Standard had no laboratory facilities at the sites. After working with hundreds of seedlings, the Institute scientists were able to isolate a specific bacterial organism similar to organisms which attacked certain plants in the United States, but sufficiently different that it had not yet been identified or classified.

Standard was so delighted that it contracted with MRI for help in setting up its own laboratories in Honduras. Ultimately, company scientists and MRI consultants developed an insecticide to control the specific insects which were carrying the microorganism to the banana plants.

In many other cases as well, initial good results with MRI brought companies back for more help. J. A. Folger and Company had been so pleased with the tastier brew developed by MRI as an instant coffee product that it came back to the Institute with another problem. Could a piece of equipment be developed which would automatically dispense steaming hot coffee?

MRI technicians and engineers invented a device which automatically weighed the correct amount of ground coffee into a brewing container. Simultaneously, heated water was poured through the grounds into a holding container which kept the coffee at a constant temperature. This synchronized action became the principle behind today's automatic drip coffeemakers.

Time and again, the coffee company returned to MRI for new projects. Between 1944 and 1963, the Folger Company, which had a roasting factory in Kansas City, contracted with MRI for projects worth over $300,000. In effect, MRI became the research and development arm for an industry with an important outlet in Kansas City.

Another firm, the Hawley and Hoops Company of Newark, New Jersey, came to MRI when its product, M&M candy, wasn't living up to its slogan, "Melts in your mouth — not in your hand." To keep from melting, the chocolate center of the candies needed a smooth coating applied as sugar syrup. Then the coating could be waxed, polished, and imprinted with the letter "M" before packaging. To be able to use this process profitably, the company had to increase production. MRI developed the prototype of an automatic method for continuously applying the special brightly colored coating to 3,300 pounds of candies per hour in an exact proportion of color and sugar for each little chocolate center. The process also reduced the need for refrigeration and lowered handling costs.

Times and projects were changing rapidly. More companies asked for help, not with microorganisms or candy coating, but with data. As MRI staff and equipment requirements expanded to meet those challenges, a new building was desperately needed.

MRI was located in a jumble of buildings in the historic Westport area where it had leased its very first space from Campbell-Taggart. The Institute was also leasing several old residences at $10 per month each. Altogether, it had six assorted structures, including the residences, the Westport fire station, a garage, and an old planing mill. There were several off-site facilities: one at a local airport; others at an ordnance works and at a nearby ballistics range. By today's standards the facilities were all primitive, but most MRI scientists could hold up for comparison only university research facilities laboratories or other modest organizational laboratories. The surroundings did not seem as hopeless then as they do to us now when we compare them to MRI's facilities today.

There was no budget for capital equipment. Every time $4,000 or $5,000 was needed for project equipment the Board of Governors had to authorize the expenditure. The largest expenditure during the early years was $10,000 for an RCA electron microscope, at that time considered state of the art. But most of the rest of the equipment was marginal. Computers were not

available to small struggling organizations such as MRI, so people worked with adding machines.

All equipment of a scientific nature had to be bought. MRI had started with nothing more than a hand-me-down set of lathes and drill presses acquired from the Kansas City School Board, which had received the equipment as war surplus property from the Kansas City plant of the Pratt and Whitney Aircraft Company. Some of these machine tools are still in the MRI shop today.

Initially, the plan had been that a sponsor would leave project equipment behind. Some of the original contracts specified that a sponsor buy equipment needed for a particular research job, and it was our understanding that the equipment would be left at MRI. Often it didn't work out that way. All the equipment obtained under these original contracts never exceeded $25,000 in value.

By 1952, it was clear that MRI was going to be financially viable and that we had to plan a permanent structure. The site on Volker Boulevard in the heart of the city had already been purchased, and a push was begun to raise construction money. Trustees Kenneth Spencer and Louis Rothschild led the drive. Many meetings with prominent Kansas Citians took place; Bruce Brewer, principal of a Kansas City advertising agency, and I wrote a booklet that answered a series of questions about why we should have a building and what effect it could have on the community. We raised approximately $1 million in less than six months, an unprecedented sum in fund raising of this sort in Kansas City at that time.

Ground was broken for construction in 1953; the original, T-shaped building was completed on the Volker site in 1955. It was altered when the west wing was built three years later.

In 1957, a 42-acre field station was donated to the Institute by W. N. Deramus, the chairman of Kansas City Southern Industries, Inc. Deramus Field Station, in Grandview on the outskirts of Kansas City, expanded to 78 acres by subsequent gifts of the Deramus family. It is currently being used for animal research in connection with toxicology programs. Originally, the land was donated with the intention of giving the Institute a site for gas turbine research. The turbines had to be isolated because they were so noisy.

As computer technology grew, so did the applications for it; the Institute's Applied Mathematics Department was very successful on a number of projects. Area companies could not afford the expensive new equipment so they turned to MRI. An early example was a special-purpose analog computer that could be used to solve problems in the construction and

The east building of the MRI complex, now known as the Kenneth A. Spencer Laboratory, was added in 1970. It came from the generosity of Mrs. Helen F. Spencer. The C. J. Patterson Memorial Library, which houses valuable holdings in scientific books and periodical literature, was given in memory of this founding Trustee by his three children.

In planning the first Volker Boulevard building, a computing room was part of the design. When MRI moved into these new facilities in 1955, approximately 5,000 square feet of floor space was allocated for a computing center, at the time the only one in the Midwest and one of the very few in the United States. Highly trained personnel were hired to translate the mathematics of problems into the computer's language.

maintenance of pipeline networks carrying water, gas, oil, and other fluids. Nationally known firms based in Kansas City made extensive use of the equipment. Companies with vast pipeline holdings such as Dow Chemical, Esso (now Exxon), and Standard Oil placed contracts with MRI that required use of the analog computer. Additionally, MRI used it to conduct studies for municipalities all over the country.

Many problems could be solved more quickly and easily, however, with digital computer equipment; for example, research topics included aircraft and missile navigation and control, aerodynamics, vibrations in buildings and machines, chemical process controls, nuclear chemistry, and the effects of noise. Sometimes problems were very specific; one project calculated the velocity at which a train of freight cars could be brought to a halt without damage to the loads they were hauling.

Market research expanded dramatically. Some companies commissioned site surveys, as did Consumers Cooperative Association (now Farmland Industries, Inc.) before locating a nitrogen fertilizer plant in Lawrence, Kansas. Other clients needed information on expanding sales territories, studies of population trends, and natural resources surveys.

The Canal Barge Company of New Orleans was interested in expanding its petroleum products operation into the chemical field and asked MRI to determine the business potential of river transportation of chemicals by barge. For this project, MRI investigated special terminal and facility requirements, capital investments, and anticipated competition. As a result of this project, the company entered this field successfully.

The Kansas Power and Light Company operated a major transmission line and several distribution lines for natural gas in Kansas and needed information for long-range planning. MRI was asked to study population trends in the area and to project both field and delivered pricing data for natural gas. The study also ascertained the impact of new appliances on the per capita consumption of gas. The final report included a projected demand for natural gas over 20 years.

MRI became active in preparing industrial development surveys for states and municipalities. During its first 10 years, the Institute had produced, through the Industrial Economics Section, the Small City Industrial Development Survey. The survey assisted communities in determining the character of their economic bases and recent economic development. The objective was to correlate industrial development with factors such as geographical location, population, transportation facilities, and distance from major cities. By surveying 500 small cities in nine states, Institute researchers gathered a body of knowledge with a potentially wide application.

Early on, federal contracts were scarce, but later the government RFP (request for proposal) became a familiar document to MRI researchers. During the 1950's, the federal government's interest in various areas of research and development increased enormously. MRI sometimes served as a subcontractor on government projects undertaken by private industry. At other times, MRI was the prime contractor for a particular government agency. One challenging project for the Air Research and Development Command of the U.S. Air Force was to develop an improved mechanism for measuring the roughness of runways. The optical beam rider that MRI developed was eventually also adapted for use by the Southern Railway as a track-leveling device.

Cancer research has been part of MRI's project direction since 1948. At that time, the National Cancer Institute (now a part of the National Institutes of Health) began to sponsor cancer research on a cooperative basis with MRI. This work was expanded by a grant from Victor E. Speas in 1952 to study chemical compounds which might control the growth of tumors. During the early stages of the Institute's involvement in cancer research, the money came from a combination of public, private, and MRI sources.

Other government-sponsored research in the 1950's included reducing small arms' smoke and flash and developing a recoilless antitank weapon for use by ground troops. Toward the end of the decade, work began in earnest on rocket fuels. Science was beginning to work feverishly in a new direction: toward the stars. And MRI, too, was ready to lift off into a new phase.

1945·1955

I n 1946, nine farsighted men signed the incorporating charter of an independent, not-for-profit research institution that would have a tremendous impact on scientific inquiry and regional development in the Midwest — and the nation.

Benjamin C. Adams, a civil engineer and chief operating officer for the Gas Service Company.

Paul D. Bartlett, grain dealer, was the first chairman of the Linda Hall Library Trusts.

Dr. Roy Cross, president, Kansas City Testing Laboratory, invented the cracking process for the fractionation of petroleum.

Robert L. Mehornay, a national spokesman for the furniture industry, Chairman of the Board of Governors from 1944-1947.

J.C. Nichols, whose Country Club Plaza shopping development is often called the nation's first shopping center, served as Chairman of MRI's Trustees from the Institute's founding in 1944 until his death in 1949.

C.J. Patterson, cereal chemist and president of Campbell-Taggart Baking, was Chairman of Trustees and Chairman of the Board of Governors, 1949-1951.

Kenneth A. Spencer, a leader in the chemical industry, chaired both the Board of Trustees, 1954-1957, and the Board of Governors, 1951-1954.

J.F. Stephens, mechanical engineer and vice president of Gustin-Bacon Manufacturing Company, one of MRI's early sponsors, was Chairman of the Board of Governors in 1948.

Charles T. Thompson, president of Thompson-Hayward Chemical Company.

MRI's dual goal was clear from the beginning: to supply needed research for industry and to encourage programs using regional resources. Several early projects focused on grains grown in the Midwest. An executive project conference on sorghum included MRI's (from left, around table) Charles Shrewsbury; Leon T. Swan, who became Senior Vice President and Chief Financial Officer; George Ward; Frank Trimble; Harold Vagtborg, the Institute's first Director and President; Martin Goland; Clayton Dohrenwend; and Carl Marberg.

(facing page) Creating fibers from molten glass was one of the Institute's earliest projects.

Gained through hard work, not magic, MRI's first project was nevertheless celebrated with good humor in an early photograph (above).

Founder J. C. Nichols and MRI President Harold Vagtborg posed in 1946 with the Institute's first electron microscope, one of the most sophisticated instruments of its day (facing page, above).

Research assistants in the Chemistry Division in 1945 (facing page, below). Most of the Institute's early projects were in the chemistry field.

36

Studying "dishpan hands" (right) helped in the evaluation of detergents for skin irritation in early MRI experiments.

Physicist Gene Moeller (below) applying rare metals in a high vacuum. All equipment had to be bought or borrowed for specific projects. At first, it was hoped that sponsors would leave equipment behind after projects were complete, but they rarely did.

Experimental centrifugal casting of printing plates for high speed presses (facing page, above).

Horse-drawn fire wagons once charged through the arched doorways that formed a backdrop for a 1947 project sponsored by Gustin-Bacon Manufacturing to develop ways to draw glass fibers for insulations and to reinforce plastics (facing page, below).

Understanding the region's natural resources was necessary. Chemist Dr. Sherman Gillam (right) in 1945 worked on one of the first soil analysis projects.

Today it is called "adaptive reuse" (below), but in the late 1940's MRI's using facilities originally built for very different purposes was just called necessity.

(facing page, above) On the historic Santa Fe Trail, MRI's first home was a building that had been the city hall and fire station of the town of Westport, Missouri. This building, and the laboratories acquired from Campbell-Taggart Research Corporation, housed MRI's chemistry and biology staff from 1945 to 1955.

Residences in the Westport area (rented for $10 a month) housed a variety of MRI functions. Building No. 5 (facing page, below, left) was home to the editorial offices of *Applied Mechanics Reviews* for which MRI took editorial responsibility in 1950 at the request of the American Society of Mechanical Engineers.

Some views from the Institute's first buildings (facing page, below right) seemed not too far removed from the days when Westport was an outfitters' station for the trails west.

Equipment was scarce in the beginning and what MRI had was often secondhand or borrowed. A 1946 electronics bench (above) looks primitive by today's standards.

The discovery of a method to keep ammonium nitrate fertilizer from caking was MRI's first big project success. In 1945, inorganic chemistry staff evaluated anti-caking agents in a humidity room.

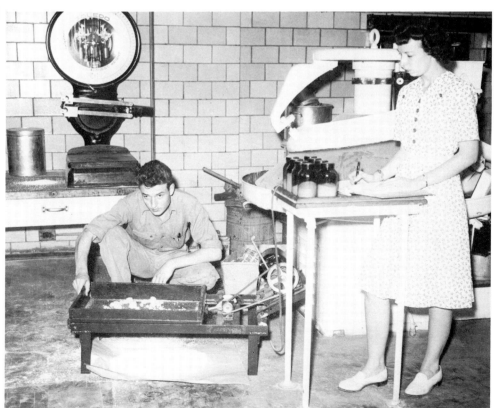

Almost every piece of equipment acquired in the early days was regarded as an important step forward. Even a grinder (above) attracted someone's interest enough for a dramatic photograph.

A permit for the Institute to handle radioactive materials came in the mid-1940's.

Recoilless rifles for the U.S. Army were developed at the nearby Sunflower Ordnance Plant.

Harold Branine and Martin Schuler (right) evaluated home laundry methods for Maytag in 1950.

(below from left) Trustee Oscar D. Nelson, Chairman of the Board, Butler Manufacturing Company; C. J. Patterson; and Kenneth A. Spencer with Charles Kimball soon after Dr. Kimball became President of the Institute in 1950.

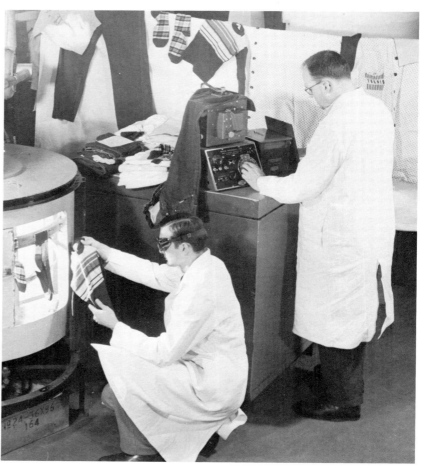

A unique method of forming iron shot was developed for the Arms and Ammunition Division of Olin-Mathiesen Chemical Corporation and patented in 1952.

Oscillograph records (left) hung up to dry were bulky forerunners of today's graphing methods.

In 1954, the staff was growing but was still small enough that the entire chemistry and chemical engineering staff could assemble together in front of the old firehouse on Pennsylvania Avenue.

The role of automobile exhaust in creating smog
was confirmed by a 1955 project sponsored by
the Southern California Air Pollution Foundation.
The effects of sunlight on engine exhaust were
measured in a greenhouse behind the Institute.

New markets for vermiculite as a soil
conditioner were the basis of a program begun
in 1951 for the Zonolite Company in Chicago.
The material is still widely used.

The physical environment at MRI was not very elegant in the early 1950's just before the new building was planned. Here the design and physical testing group works in secondhand surroundings on programs in vibration elimination and ballistics.

Staff members in the home economics section evaluated restaurant equipment, conducted food-related studies, and experimented with detergents, laundry methods, and coffee brewing.

Regional minerals, clays, glass sands, and other commercial products were extensively evaluated in the first ten years.

After the 1951 flood, the worst in Kansas City's history, MRI researchers used stress gauges attached to oil storage tanks to measure possible stress fracture.

Paul Constant, electrical engineer (left), worked with the hydraulic analog computer planning water distributing systems in Iowa, Kansas, Mississippi, and Nebraska (1952).

The management team in 1952: (top row, from left) Perry L. Bidstrup, Sherman Gillam, Frederick Stephens, William Niven, Robert Hancox, Price Wickersham; (bottom row) Max Thornton, Leon T. Swan, Charles Kimball, Martin Goland.

Inside half-raised walls (above), the combined Executive and Building committees inspected the site of the new Volker Boulevard building in 1953.

Trustees (left to right) William Deramus, Sr., Louis S. Rothschild, R. Crosby Kemper, Sr., and Kenneth A. Spencer with a preliminary model of the building.

(facing page) The initial Volker Boulevard building (1955) was named for Charles N. Kimball when he retired as President in 1975.

GROWTH
AND
CHANGE

FROM THE MIDWEST TO THE MOON

From the Institute's founding until the early sixties, the majority of MRI's clients were Midwestern-based manufacturing and distributing companies. Although public sector contracts had been increasing, most of the funds that came into MRI during these years were from private industry. But by 1961, the role of MRI in government research was changing; and, like everything else on the scientific scene in those years, it was changing rapidly.

One morning in October 1957, Americans listening to their radios heard little beeps, the sounds of Sputnik, man's first orbiting satellite, sent up by Russia. Immediately Congressmen wondered what was wrong with American technology, that the nation had lagged behind in making this vault into the future, and they shifted federal money to space research and to other kinds of scientific and technical investigation.

We got into the space race at MRI through a call from Senator Stuart Symington. Martin Schuler and I went to Washington and made a proposal to James E. Webb, recently named head of the National Aeronautics and Space Administration (NASA); soon we were involved in technology utilization. Webb believed that the Midwest was more representative in its potential to the industrial application responses of space technology than the more "sophisticated" Northeast. He wanted the work done by an institution with proven links to the private sector. Projects generated out of the space program introduced the Institute — and indeed the entire

nation — to the concept of technology transfer.

Much of the new space-derived technical information was potentially useful to private industry and business, but few of those who could use the information had the time to retrieve it or the capacity to adjust it for their own needs. This gap created a need for brokers between the producers and potential users of the new technology, and a research institute such as MRI was admirably suited to take this role.

The new function ultimately came to be known as technology transfer. It had been performed by MRI — without the benefit of a catchy phrase to call it — from the very beginning. We had always been able to adapt what had been learned on one investigation to answer other diverse inquiries. One example of effective technology transfer was the project to measure runway roughness for the Air Force that led to a track-leveling device for the Southern Railway.

In 1957, the same year as Sputnik, President Eisenhower called a national White House Conference on Technical and Distribution Research for the benefit of small businesses, for which I had served as deputy chairman. There we outlined two principal problems small businesses faced in using research effectively. One was their limited understanding of the importance of research, and the other was a misunderstanding of the complex nature of research itself. To stay competitive, small businesses needed technology, and they could have it if they knew what to look for and whom to ask. They needed the results of research, not the practice of research itself. The answers to the questions business had about development were already there; all that needed planning was the transfer of the information.

As a result of this conference and increased governmental and private research funding in response to Sputnik, MRI became a major information broker for technology transfer.

In 1961, when the first project for NASA in space technology utilization came to MRI, the Institute set about formally to develop techniques for the transfer of space innovations and discoveries to industry. Out of this work, many devices and processes were invented or improved for use by companies in such areas as the manufacture of vaccines, hearing aids, and aircraft controls, and in the development of cost-reduction methods and quality control structures.

The Trustees of MRI arranged that several members of the MRI staff should visit 20 cities in the Midwest to explain what we were doing with technology transfer. The Institute's most important single product has always been information, and at this time we were able to serve industry well by making presentations. In plain language that industrial leaders appreciated, the Institute explained the new products and processes that could be successfully utilized or adapted for use in Midwestern plants.

Some of the most well-known examples of this transfer occurred in the use of transistors, which led to the miniaturization of electronic circuitry that eventually made possible electronic typesetting for newspapers, home computers, and other "miracles" of the modern age. The microwave technology explored for World War II led to improved telephone circuits and cable television, not to mention microwave ovens or pacemakers. Not all technology transfer resulted in new devices, of course. Management technology, now widely used in American business, also benefited from the transfer of information from federal projects.

As potentially valuable as so many transfers were, they did not happen quickly. Even a relatively straightforward adaptation — the jet engine of a military plane adapted to a commercial airliner — had earlier taken a decade. Of all the tyrannies that have oppressed mankind, none has been so difficult to overthrow as our resistance to change. That resistance, much more than the complexities of science, has slowed the reach of new technology into private industry.

Before technology transfers could reach peak efficiency, there needed to be a better climate for transfer, with more receptivity to innovation. Also, a lack of creativity caused transfer barriers when potential users saw changes as alarmingly radical.

This attitude was worsened when the information was shared in jargon that kept the user from learning what technology was actually available. Moreover, decision-makers in a business were often hesitant to change from a product that was profitable even when they saw that better products could be developed. Lack of long-range planning was another deterrent to technology transfer; without foresight in product development the effectiveness of the transfer was lost.

MRI was able to break through some of the resistance to change because it could point to a successful history of producing valuable results for sponsors. Additionally, the Institute did not obscure its results from a client and never has. Since the sponsor controls patents and other results, it is the sponsor's choice to make the new information available more broadly. While MRI always honored the privacy of its client relationships, it was still able to participate in a natural diffusion of information as pleased sponsors shared their good news.

Today, MRI manages, as one of its major projects, the Solar Energy Research Institute headquartered in Golden, Colorado. An important responsibility at SERI is the transfer of information about solar energy

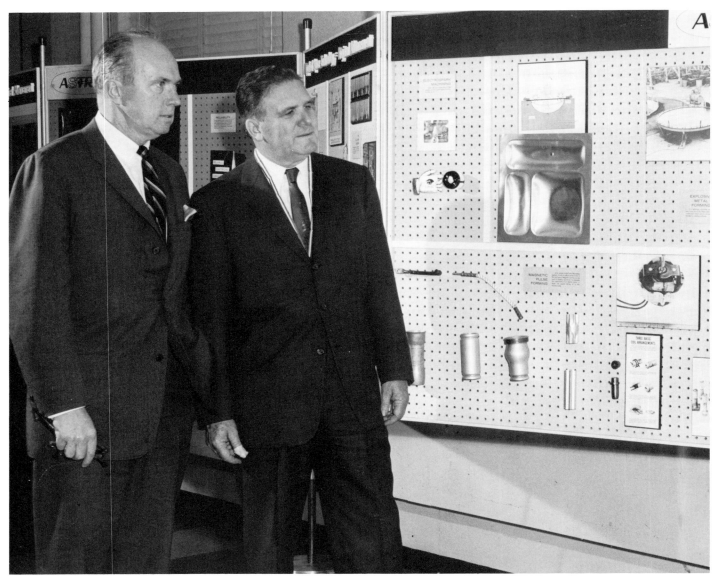

MRI's ASTRA technology transfer project for NASA in 1961 was the first in the U.S.; James A. Webb, first administrator of NASA on the right.

and other alternative forms of energy production that will help increase America's independence from non-U.S. energy sources. Consistent with its mission and as part of its research programs, SERI makes the resulting scientific and technological information available to universities, state and local governments, and appropriate private sector organizations.

These ongoing efforts in technology transfer include technical reports, papers at professional conferences, articles in scholarly and professional journals, as well as collaborative research with colleagues in universities and in-

dustry. The personal interaction of SERI researchers with universities is one effective means of sharing SERI's experience and discoveries in solar energy. SERI's cooperation with solar energy projects throughout the country and its outreach to potential users of solar technologies are a logical outgrowth of the way MRI has always viewed its role in sharing information. Indeed, the Institute was successful in its bid for the SERI contract in large part because of its early efforts in technology transfer, beginning in the 1950's when the term was new in the vocabulary of science.

THE PROFESSION OF SCIENCE

In June 1950, the staff numbered 88. Ten years later, it had grown to 248, still not a very large number considering the projects we faced by that time. In the early years, we grew without benefit of advertising for trained personnel, yet we had no problem recruiting. At one time, most of our staff came from the Midwest, specifically from Big Eight universities, but as the Economics Division grew in the late 1950's the proportions changed. Soon the degree of diversification was remarkable, and MRI boasted staff from more than 100 universities across the land.

A scientist who succeeds at a research institute must be an interesting amalgam of skills and attitudes. A research institute is not any place for an observer, or, on the other hand, for someone who wants to redefine Einstein's theory of relativity. Institute work often means setting aside the specialized interest that was all-absorbing during one's thesis or dissertation years, and turning to whatever problem is at hand.

Many people at MRI are doing things that they never dreamed of doing a decade ago. Researchers don't move deliberately and self-consciously from one discipline to another, but they may begin the shift to a new scientific activity by working on the fringes of some other program. Professional growth is evolutionary, and a number of individuals over time at MRI have developed impressive generalist backgrounds. Through the years, MRI has seen the emergence of a new type within a research institute: the professional who is flexible, who is interested in the scientific method irrespective of the particular science to which it seems technically to belong. Research institutes are the ideal environment for such individuals to develop to their fullest capabilities.

Beyond the scientific skills needed for work at the Institute, a senior researcher must also be able to market our product. Marketing science is a difficult proposition at best, but the entire senior staff of MRI is involved in the business of developing new business. A senior technical person's time, on the average, is spent 75 percent in research; the remaining 25 percent goes to writing proposals, to attending client conferences, to preparing papers for professional societies, and similar activities.

The use of titles for managerial staff has evolved since the early days. Originally, managerial titles were derived from university usage, for example, "Chairman" of a department. A transition was gradually made from university terminology to titles similar to those in business and industry: first "Director" of a division, then "Manager."

Of course, a research institute needs highly qualified people who want to remain in research. In the early sixties, the title of "Senior" was set up to designate scientists who could advance in position and earnings without having to become managers. About 30 such professionals have been promoted further, to the position of "Principal"; together, these individuals constitute the MRI Council of Principal Scientists. A select few outstanding scientists are designated

Senior Advisors in their particular field of expertise.

The Council of Principal Scientists works to advance professional development within the Institute. Council members are, in effect, aides to the directors and other managers of MRI. Because they are close to their fields on a day-to-day basis and also have a broad overview, they are often the first to identify opportunities in new research areas that can be developed into important programs.

From the beginning, MRI has been active in professional societies. Martin Goland edited the journal *Applied Mechanics Reviews* during the early 1950's. MRI scientists made up the majority of the membership of the local chapter of the American Chemical Society. Institute personnel also contributed heavily to the development of the local chapter of Electrical and Electronic Engineers. As part of these professional activities, the staff prepared a large number of scientific papers. At one point, with fewer than 200 persons on staff, more than 100 articles were printed in the scientific literature in a year's time.

But even these activities were pursued with attention to economy. Since its first days in the old firehouse, MRI has operated on the lean side in staffing. Throughout the years the proportion of researchers to administrative personnel has been two to one, allowing the Institute to meet its expenses while adding new programs.

Still, the Institute was required to continue expanding its physical operations to house the growing staff and program needs. In the late 1950's, MRI acquired the Barstow School, consisting of three buildings and three acres of land immediately southeast of the Volker Boulevard building. The school had moved to a new location and its site had been part of the original bequest of William Rockhill Nelson which provided that the land once belonging to his extensive estate could not be sold for commercial purposes. The school's old dormitory was torn down, but into its main building went MRI's

growing Economics and Management Science Division. The gymnasium became the first MRI building named for a person, MRI's Technical Director, Max Thornton, and is today still in use for staff recreation and meetings.

If the Institute staff and facilities were expanding as the decade of the sixties began, it was only in keeping with the expanding horizons of MRI projects. Ahead in the next 15 years were some of MRI's greatest challenges and most exciting discoveries. The opportunities for research were mushrooming; MRI had come of age and was fully ready to participate in whatever new directions might open.

Research in the United States had grown from an $800 million business in 1949 to a $13 billion business in 1960. Large-scale research was entering its second generation, and so was MRI. Each year enough scientific papers were being written to fill seven complete sets of the *Encyclopedia Britannica*. Scientists faced a mountainous task of making practical use of all this knowledge, and few places were so well prepared as MRI to take part in the process of turning research into solutions to the problems of industry and society.

In its first 19 years, MRI served 1,000 different clients. In the next 15, it added only about 250 new different companies or agencies as sponsors, yet the dollar volume increased and held stable far above the volume of the 1960's. During the sixties, MRI's sponsor list began to take on a different face, increasingly governmental. The number of multiyear projects increased dramatically. It was not that private sector projects decreased, for they stayed at about the same volume; instead, the number of government projects grew tremendously.

Not only the federal government but also state and local governments became increasingly sophisticated about buying research. They allocated money for projects in criminal justice, regional development, and environmental impact. During the 15 years from 1960 to 1975,

MRI worked on an enormous range of projects, from the development of equipment to aid in lunar landing to the tracking down of the bacteria responsible for salmonella poisoning. MRI stood with a foot in each camp. The Institute might work for the government in water pollution, but private companies still trusted MRI as a knowledgeable and useful resource on the same subject.

As American science sought to make good John F. Kennedy's pledge of 1961 to have a man on the moon within a decade, the Institute became increasingly involved in space-related programs. For example, a computer program was designed to predict the thermal behavior of nozzles and control devices of spacecraft in orbit. The program proved especially useful to Project Apollo, other lunar programs, and the *Voyager* probes near Saturn and Uranus.

In 1962-63, MRI sent teams to universities in Alabama, Florida, Georgia, Kentucky, Mississippi, South Carolina, and Tennessee, as well as to Big Eight schools in the Midwest, to acquaint them with the research needs and interests of NASA and the opportunities for research support open to faculty members and administrators. Another MRI team assisted in the transfer of aerospace-generated technology applications, assessing areas for transfer. Abstracts of identified problems were circulated to NASA research centers and to aerospace contractors. After interviews and investigation, material on the problems and the potential solutions was sent to individuals and organizations which could benefit from the available technology. Aerospace technology was applied then to biomedical concerns, water pollution, weather controls, and sewage disposal.

Because MRI was primarily in the technology and technology transfer business, the Institute's social scientists worked with physical scientists to investigate the trauma that many people experience when certain kinds of technological information are made public. They looked closely at the roles taken by the government agencies, industries, and professional bodies which publicized new developments, including information about environmental pollutants, foods and drugs, medicines and medical practices, hazardous consumer products, and energy needs, as well as agricultural practices, recreation and cultural activities, and law enforcement and national defense developments.

Young mathematicians at work in the 1960's.

MRI became steadily more involved in programs assessing the effects on people of environmental, social, and ecological — as well as technological — factors. MRI social scientists conducted a number of projects aimed at discovering in what states and cities the "good life" was most likely to occur. Using criteria developed by a Presidential Commission on the quality of life, including over 100 social, economic, environmental, and political factors, the research isolated categories ranging from individual status to quality of state and local governments. Carried on over a period of years, the study had provocative results. For example, Minnesota, second of the top five states in the first study, dropped to 13th place when the study was updated in 1972. Such changes were not only controversial, but they helped stimulate self-evaluation on the part of states and the individuals who lived in those states.

In the area of energy conservation and alternative energy sources, MRI conducted numerous studies including evaluating the feasibility of using solar energy as a means of generating on-site electric power. Both photovoltaic and solar thermal systems were considered, and the elements of 12 potential systems were studied for technological and economic feasibility. A timetable was produced for possible implementation from 1974 to 2000.

In seeking alternative energy sources, the U.S. Environmental Protection Agency contracted with MRI for an evaluation of the St. Louis Union Electric Refuse Fuel Project. The eastern Missouri utility company was experimenting with the use of a mixture of shredded refuse and coal in its Meramec Power Plant. MRI assumed responsibility for evaluating the operating characteristics of the plant, the air pollution resulting from the process, and the level of emissions generated.

Other environmental projects included ranking the total impact of several types of beverage containers on environmental quality. Factors studied and compared included natural resources used in production, energy consumption, waterborne waste, and atmospheric emissions.

MRI also studied human problems. Biofeedback, the measurement of physical reactions which go on constantly within a person's body, became a focus of numerous experiments. Biofeedback research shows that pain changes body temperatures in some parts of the body while the pain is being experienced in other parts. By regulating the temperature changes in prescribed ways, a person can control some of the pain which triggered the changes in the first place. Using biofeedback, hypnosis, and other techniques, MRI conducted experiments to alleviate the pain suffered by cancer patients, as well as the pain of migraine headaches.

MRI's extensive cancer research included a program to evaluate the complex psychological and physical factors affecting women who have breast cancer. A series of workshops brought together cancer patients and interdisciplinary teams of experts nationally and internationally recognized in their fields. Many previously undocumented psychological factors experienced by breast cancer patients were identified, and a model of acceptable procedures for treatment was developed. The use of this model by physicians and other professionals has led to a more enlightened patient population and, in many instances, more rapid recovery by these patients.

In 1964, the Institute began working with the U.S. Arms Control and Disarmament Agency. MRI's research was concerned primarily with developing procedures relating to the inspection of the production, transportation, and storage of chemical and biological weapons. Means of agent identification were formulated as an aid to the inspection of another nation's chemical store, to ensure compliance with disarmament agreements.

When arms control became an issue of increasing importance in the sixties, the Institute developed a simple way of determining a nation's compliance with arms control agreements. Institute researchers were concerned that a country would attempt evasion of limitations. They recommended surveillance methods including various indicators such as transportation of basic chemicals, power consumption, and other barometers of unusual industrial activity. This body of research proved especially valuable when the United States negotiated with the Soviet Union for Strategic Arms Limitation Talks (SALT) in the 1970's.

An entirely different research focus, also in the sixties, related to the recreation and leisure industry. In 1967-68, MRI conducted inventories of existing public and private recreation facilities for Kansas, Missouri, Colorado, Minnesota, Arkansas, and Tennessee. Supply and demand were carefully correlated to identify how many additional facilities might be desirable. MRI developed consulting services to help states establish systematic planning efforts for their recreational needs.

Having been immersed in this unusual accumulation of data on various consumer interests in all aspects of recreation, MRI was able to assemble a multiclient program, the largest multisponsored project in the Institute's history. Approximately 30 clients from the private sector, including such companies as American Express, Boise Cascade, Sears Roebuck, and Ford Motor Company, jointly funded and shared the research which was valuable to their future marketing plans.

In 1968, several mergers of railroads in the Midwest and Southwest were proposed. Some of these were potentially damaging to a smaller regional line, the Denver and Rio Grande-Western, which contracted with MRI to study the possible impact of the mergers. The Institute staff participated in hearings before the Interstate Commerce Commission considering matters of rail traffic growth, rail competition within the central transcontinental corridor, and individual markets important to the Denver and Rio Grande-Western line. Partially as a result of these studies, the ICC ruled against the proposed mergers, and the Denver and Rio Grande-Western remained a viable small shipper in the western United States.

Other projects concerned with regional commerce included the new international airport begun in Kansas City in 1967. MRI developed a comprehensive total plan for construction activities based on the critical path method, evaluating construction schedules, timing of contracts, decision requirements at every phase, coordination with other agencies, and cash flow analysis and projections. As construction proceeded, MRI provided the Kansas City Aviation Department with a status report each month for city personnel to review. The resulting three-terminal airport, built on time and within budget, will be capable of handling the region's air traffic needs until well past the year 2000.

In the seventies, MRI became increasingly involved in projects reflecting society's newer needs and problems. A new menace to highway safety, drugs of various kinds, led to the Institute's development of methods for analyzing samples of blood, bile, and face and finger washings from fatally injured drivers, and the development of specimen acquisition kits. These kits were distributed to cooperating coroners and medical examiners and quickly became a widely accepted means of screening 44 commonly used drugs, among them marijuana and alcohol.

It was important to the growth of the Institute and to its loyalty to the original charter for MRI to become active in community outreach of all significant kinds. From the beginning of the Institute the leadership of the region was involved in the affairs of MRI, and MRI in the affairs of the region. It was a happy symbiotic partnership, unique in the history of research institutes, and it continues to be important to MRI and to the Midwest today.

The relationship of MRI to other institutions has been encouraging at every phase of the Institute's development, and, it is fair to say, this relationship has been important to the growth and prosperity of the other institutions as well. We have been closest in depth and continuity of relationship to the Linda Hall Library of Science and Technology. The night in 1945 that Dr. Joseph C. Shipman got off the train in Kansas City to become librarian at Linda Hall coincided with the first annual meeting of the MRI Trustees, which he attended. He was, until his death in 1977, a powerful force in building a great library, and a valuable leader in the development of the Institute. He once said that if all but one of the scientific journals of the world were to be destroyed and it was necessary to retain the essence of everything that had been important in science, the files of the proceedings of the Royal Society of London should be chosen as the last survivor. Only 10 complete runs are extant in the world (the others were destroyed in the great fire of London in 1660). One is held by Linda Hall, along with a great many historical editions and a superb collection of scientific books secured by the Library under Joe Shipman's supervision.

These two independent, freestanding, unrelated institutions, Linda Hall and MRI, both dedicated to science and technology, are within a few hundred yards of each other, creating the nucleus of the science community in Kansas City, which today consists of approximately 25,000 persons. More than one industry has elected to move to Kansas City, or to expand operations here, because of the combined presence of MRI and Linda Hall.

Another institution with close ties to MRI over the years has been the University of Kansas City (as it was known before it became the University of Missouri-Kansas City in 1963). Close to the Institute geographically and intellectually, UKC was a privately supported institution whose graduate faculty often worked at MRI to supplement their salaries and to complement their professional interests. MRI helped UKC move into graduate studies and supplied some of the graduate faculty. I served as a trustee for many years and when the decision was made to move the University of Kansas City into the Missouri system, the merger was negotiated by a committee made up of trustees and long-time advisors to MRI.

Over the years, MRI has had fruitful exchanges with the Kansas University Medical Center in Kansas City, Kansas. These began when then Chancellor of the University, Franklin D. Murphy, and I agreed in the early 1950's on the pressing need for graduate courses in engineering. These were held at the Medical Center facilities with professional staff from the KU campus in Lawrence commuting to teach students from the technical staffs of Bendix, TWA, Westinghouse, MRI, and other scientifically oriented Kansas City companies. Hundreds of people earned master's degrees in four or five engineering curricula through this relationship.

Other colleges and universities in the area,

particularly Kansas State University, have shared interests with MRI in relationships of great value to the development of the Institute. K-State offered course work in agricultural engineering and participated in lectures on agricultural economics important to this region and, therefore, to the Institute. MRI also assisted in establishing the Kansas City Regional Council for Higher Education (KCRCHE), a consortium of metropolitan colleges which was designed for the sharing of facilities and the solving of problems.

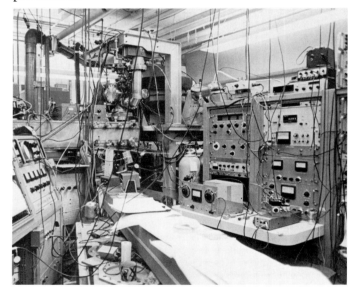

Rockhurst College has also been significant to MRI. I served on Rockhurst's first board of regents in 1958, and Father Maurice Van Ackeren, Rockhurst's Chancellor, has been a Trustee of the Institute for many years. A number of alumni from Rockhurst have come to MRI to work, and the college has an active work-study program that brings young people to the Institute during the school year and for the summer to work 15 hours a week in their respective areas of skill and training.

The relationship of MRI to other research institutes around the country has also been critical to our growth. In the early 1950's, Ed Weidlein, who was president of the Mellon Institute, suggested that the presidents of major research institutes should get together annually and that business managers should meet biannually. Some of the benefits that have come from these conferences include uniformity of data handling, identification of common problems, and exchange of information on costs and personnel matters.

A number of key personnel in one research institute have accepted appointments at another, and MRI has provided personnel for several of these types of exchanges. The first and second presidents of Southwest Research Institute came from MRI, and one of the presidents of the Mellon Institute was an MRI alumnus. An MRI alumnus became president of North Star Research Institute prior to its merger with MRI.

This merger is an example of the cooperation that exists among research institutes. In

technology-based firms in the Twin Cities area. MRI's merger with North Star came too late in its history to solve enough problems for success; and after two years, MRI returned all properties to the North Star Board.

During the sixties and seventies MRI flourished. The staff and facilities expanded to meet the demands of a rich variety of sponsors and interests. The Institute did valuable work exploring natural resources, protecting the environment, and finding uses important to individuals and to society for technology in its many forms.

In these busy and exciting decades, the questions asked by the founders a quarter cen-

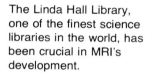

The Linda Hall Library, one of the finest science libraries in the world, has been crucial in MRI's development.

1975, MRI acquired North Star Research Institute of Minneapolis as a result of having managed its affairs for 18 months at the request of the North Star Board. At this time, all North Star assets were transferred to MRI, with provisions for their restricted use. MRI put management personnel in place along with newly hired professionals, and erected a new headquarters building. Regrettably, although North Star, which had been founded in 1963, had the same general objectives as MRI, it never fully matured, despite the concentration of

tury earlier about the functions a research institute might serve were fully answered. Often the answers were found in projects and sponsors that could have been but dimly imagined in the beginning. Who would have thought that a research organization which started with a fertilizer project would be working on lunar landing modules only 20 years later? One of MRI's most exhilarating discoveries was the wide variety of projects it could successfully complete as it helped make the vital link between science and industry in the Midwest.

1955
1965

Charles Grosskreutz, Principal Advisor for Physics (left), and Gordon Shaw, Senior Electron Microscopist.

Packaging projects were numerous during the late 1950's and early 1960's. A unique technique for sealing flexible packaging for the Quartermaster Corps created seals three times stronger than existing seals.

Important contributions to the administrative functions of MRI were made by Sarah Lechtman (left), Librarian and Corporate Secretary, who structured the first technical library and developed the first policies and procedures manual for MRI; Viola Kelley, Supervisor of Stenographic Services, who set up the techniques and formats for preparing proposals and reports to clients; and Marilyn Thomas (right), Personnel Administrator, who established systems for personnel actions.

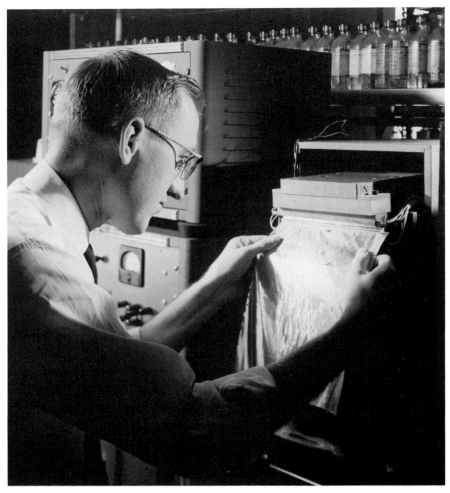

In the early 1960's, MRI worked with the University of Kansas on a bioengineering project to develop a blood oxygenation device for use in cardiac surgery. Trustees Miller Nichols (left) and James M. Kemper (right) look over a model with Dr. Kimball and Hugh H. Harrison, Hibbing, Minnesota, sponsor of the project.

William B. House, Director of the Biology Division, conducted an early study on aging.

At the Kansas City airport, Senator Stuart Symington accompanied by Charles Kimball greeted Senator Hubert Humphrey and former President Harry S. Truman when Senator Symington conferred with Missouri agricultural leaders in 1958.

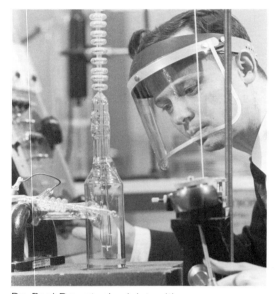

Dr. Paul Bryant, physicist, with ultrahigh vacuum apparatus.

New methods of measuring air speeds of helicopters were found for Bell Helicopter Corporation, Fort Worth, Texas, in 1959.

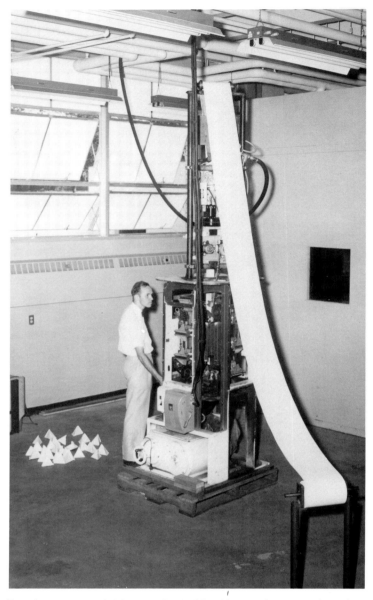

Development model for tetrahedral liquid containers monitored by David Bendersky (above), Principal Engineer.

Flash photolysis equipment was used to study the nature of flames to develop fire-extinguishing agents for the Ansul Company, Marinette, Wisconsin.

Senator John F. Kennedy was the principal speaker at a Rockhurst College convocation in 1956. MRI has shared special relationships with Rockhurst and other area colleges and universities.

President Dwight D. Eisenhower called a White House conference on research and development for small business in 1956. Dr. Kimball and Arthur Motley (right), publisher of *Parade* magazine, served as co-chairmen.

Hawley and Hoops Company of Newark, New Jersey, came to MRI for a candy coating that could live up to M&M's slogan, "Melts in your mouth—not in your hand."

The accident rate for aircraft landing on carriers at sea led to the U.S. Navy's program at MRI to develop methods of tracking wind speeds and gusts to reduce these hazards (below).

(facing page, above) During the late 1950's, MRI turned considerable attention to problems of metal fatigue. Physicist Ansel Stubbs evaluates physical changes in a glove box protected from the atmosphere.

Development model for encapsulating electronic solenoids (facing page, below).

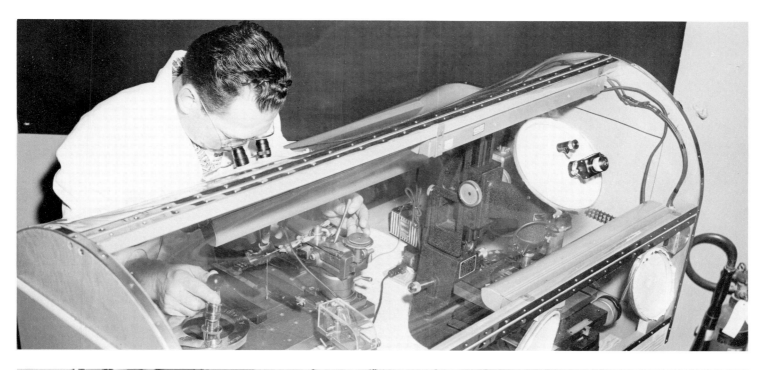

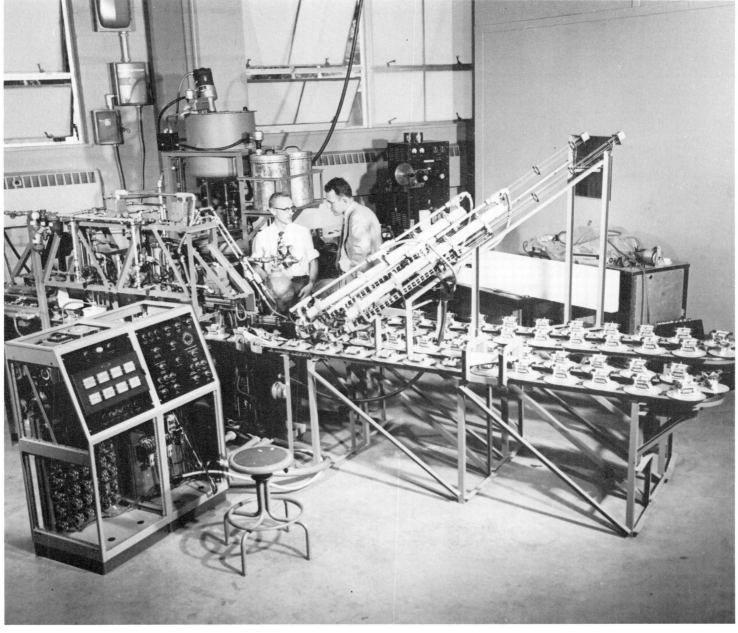

Institute engineers evaluated mechanical performance for the U.S. Army's Overland Train, an off-road cargo carrier.

An early economics study determined the benefit of improving the Missouri River channel for barge transportation. In the 1960's, economics became an increasingly important field at MRI.

Bioengineering done in collaboration with the Kansas University Medical Center resulted in an early heart-lung machine, a forerunner of those used in cardiac surgery today. MRI's cooperative activities with various universities and colleges have been important to the growth of the Institute, and to the strengthening of scientific research throughout the region.

Without access to Linda Hall Library of Science and Technology's extensive scientific holdings, the Institute could never have flourished as it has. Joseph C. Shipman (shown here in the library's rare books room), director of the Library from 1944 to 1974, guided its development.

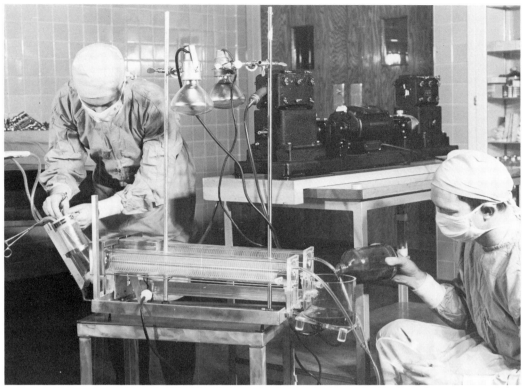

71

A project undertaken for the State of Nebraska involved developing an edible, water-soluble food packaging made from special starch ingredients (right).

(below, right) Still called the Barstow building, the main building of the Barstow School was built in 1928 and acquired by MRI in 1962.

(below, left) Mrs. Charles N. Kimball (left), Mrs. Kenneth A. Spencer, and Mrs. Richard King Mellon (right) in the Spencer Auditorium during the visit of the Mellons at MRI's Annual Meeting in 1964. Mrs. Spencer's generosity made possible the Kenneth A. Spencer building, an expansion of MRI on the Volker site. The Mellon Fund, administered by MRI's Board of Directors, was a result of a generous gift of $500,000 by Richard King Mellon in recognition of MRI's achievements.

(facing page, above) In 1960, the State of Nebraska initiated an extensive research program to develop new industrial outlets for nonfood uses of farm products. (from left) Frank Morrison, governor of Nebraska; Dr. Buell Beadle; Pearle Finigan, Director of Economic Development for Nebraska; Dr. Max Thornton; and Dr. Kimball met at MRI to discuss the program.

(facing page, below) Division Directors in 1960: (left to right) Dr. Warren E. Snyder, Engineering; Dr. Max H. Thornton, Vice President and Technical Director; Dr. Kimball; Dr. Sheldon Levy, Mathematics and Physics; and Dr. Buell W. Beadle, Chemistry.

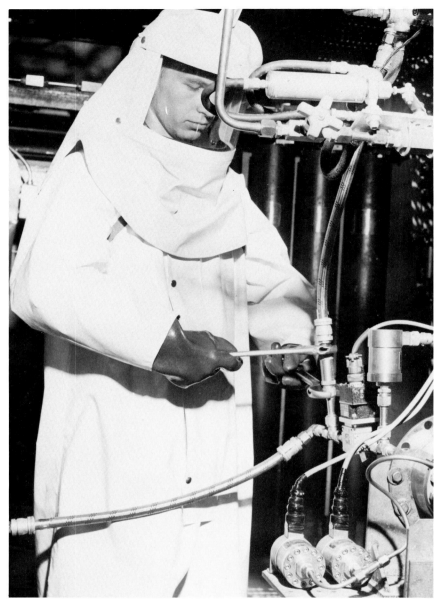

A scale model of the *Apollo* (facing page) was used to study the effect of sun on the spacecraft. Studies simulating the sun's heat showed that spacecraft could be slowly rotated to distribute heat and cold. This discovery is still important to space exploration today.

MRI's successful development of survival rations (below, right) led to a new research program in high-energy spaceflight foods.

Cancer research has been important at MRI since the 1940's. In the 1960's the cancer chemotherapy team (below, left) headed by Dr. C. C. Cheng (left in lower row) synthesized compounds for screening by the National Cancer Institute.

High-energy boron fuels (left) were developed by Callery Chemical Company for the U.S. Navy in 1962 through a project with MRI.

EXPANDING HORIZONS

INTERFACE
WITH
TOMORROW

Social analysts seem fond of looking back now on the 1970's as the decade of the "me generation," but MRI was probably more outwardly directed during those years than at any time in its history. The projects during the seventies took on more characteristics of outreach and were potentially more beneficial to the human community at large, and in far-reaching terms. Solar energy, environmental interests, medical research, conservation of natural and human resources — each vast research area has implications for all of us personally.

At the beginning of its second quarter-century, the Institute had reached maturity. It was taking a role in the scientific community — both locally and nationally — providing useful problem-solving techniques to clients and answering society's questions.

MRI gained some valuable insights in working on projects for both the public and private sectors. The Institute's business relationships with the federal government subsequently led to invitations that allowed us to bring some of those insights to bear on a variety of national needs. I was nominated by Congressman Larry Winn of Kansas to join the Technical Advisory Committee of the Office of Technology Assessment in 1977, the first person from the Midwest to join the 10-person Committee. I served as Chairman from 1980 to 1984. OTA has a sophisticated staff and is governed by a board of six Senators and six Congressmen. It is one of the

principal technology advisory groups to the U.S. Congress.

The relationships of MRI and the governments of numerous states have been ongoing and fruitful. We have important liaison with the governments of Kansas and Missouri, and have had this liaison since the Institute's founding. All state governments in our own region can directly benefit from the Institute's expertise in planning, and a number of them have done so. For example, MRI worked with Nebraska through a series of projects funded by a unique state tax, the proceeds of which were directed toward finding nonfood uses for agricultural products. MRI developed a soluble, edible packaging film from cornstarch, and the material was then manufactured by a large company which located a processing facility in Nebraska. MRI also developed several plant growth stimulators as part of this project for Nebraska.

We were able to work effectively with groups of states, notably through the Rocky Mountain Governors' Conference and a similar group of the governors of the Great Plains states. Projects in each instance were to find effective economic uses of the respective region's natural resources and higher education capabilities.

But almost all such programs are initiated less formally between individuals than between states or their large beauracracies and MRI. Many of the relationships MRI has developed have begun with a meeting with one person who recognized in MRI the possible answer to a question that needed raising.

In 1951, I joined the Young Presidents' Organization, which at that time had only 125 members, and not another of them was in the research institute business. The relationships established with other members of YPO gave MRI access to many people who would not otherwise have heard of it. Since the requirement for belonging at that time was that a member had to become, before his 39th birthday, president of a company doing $1 million worth of business, acquaintances from that organization often had real need to become involved with the Institute over the years. Through YPO, dozens of persons have come to MRI as trustees, benefactors, and clients. Since Young Presidents are no longer considered young after their 49th birthday, after 1960 I joined its alumni group called the Chief Executives Forum. YPO membership has grown from an initial 100 members to more than 5,000, but the CEF numbers only several hundred members, many of whom have become part of the MRI "family."

When technology transfer became an important password in the scientific community in the early sixties, J. Herbert Hollomon, Assistant Secretary of Commerce for Science and Technology, suggested a series of conferences for engineers, rather like the Gordon Conferences in New Hampshire that concentrated on the sciences. The engineering conferences, sponsored by the Engineering Foundation, were held annually at the Proctor Academy in Andover, New Hampshire, with MRI closely involved from the beginning; in fact, we organized and chaired the first four annual sessions. Our subject was how to move technology ahead — how to get it going and how to get it used.

Although by now the Institute was working on regional and national tasks, there were also programs close to home that fulfilled the spirit of the original charter in important ways. One such local effort was Science Pioneers, still

today perhaps the single most influential sustained program for encouraging science learning in the metropolitan area schools.

Originally, science fairs were organized in communities as a result of the influence of a syndicated group in Washington called "Science Service," which was formed to stimulate interest among science teachers and students. In Kansas City, the Kansas City Museum held these events initially, but as more display and exhibit space was required, the facilities there proved inadequate. In the fifties, the Kansas City Star, MRI, and a number of interested citizens collaborated to found a not-for-profit organization, Science Pioneers, with the mission of raising funds to allow the Science Fair to be held in the Municipal Auditorium, where it has been held ever since. MRI has always administered the Science Fair. The first three presidents of Science Pioneers were associated with MRI: Max Thornton, Joseph Shipman of the Linda Hall Library, and Martin Schuler. Many of the judges for the Science Fair have come from MRI, and we have twice acted as host for the International Science Fair, in which winners of all local and regional fairs compete. The Greater Kansas City area's organizational model of Science Pioneers has been emulated in dozens of cities in the United States and abroad; today, the Greater Kansas City Science and Engineering Fair is the largest of its kind in the United States.

Science Pioneers sponsors a number of allied activities such as lectures by members of the scientific community. Seminars are scheduled during the school year on Saturday mornings once a month, and for the last five years have been held at MRI.

In addition, the Wellington Lecture Series has brought speakers of national reputation to Kansas City for Science Pioneers. The lecture series is named for C. G. Wellington, Executive Editor of the Kansas City Star, a founder of Science Pioneers who left a bequest to finance such a series.

Over the years, MRI had developed into a leader in programs relating to the progress of metropolitan areas and it was only natural to turn some of that expertise and interest toward our home city. Able to evaluate the productive and nonproductive points of other leadership programs in other cities, the Institute became involved with Kansas City Tomorrow, a training program of the Civic Council designed to train young professionals to be the city leaders of the future. For two years, the Institute taught these young people by exposing them to established leaders one day each month for a year of study in education, health care delivery, city government, private sector growth, and all the other elements of a city's development. Now in its eighth year, and directed by a professional leadership consultant, the program's alumni number several hundred, many of whom have served in special public service assignments.

"Prime Time" is a phrase that was coined in the early seventies to describe a public relations effort by Kansas City leaders on behalf of area residents. Of the original Prime Time Steering Committee of a dozen persons, many were MRI Trustees; the Committee held monthly breakfast meetings at MRI for several years. The point of the program was to overcome Kansas City's so-called cowtown image and gain the city recognition nationwide. And it has worked.

Largely through the efforts of Prime Time, the national press has turned attention to Kansas City increasingly over the last decade. In 1976, the chairman of the Mutual Benefit Life Insurance Company of Newark, New Jersey, stated that his company's decision to locate its western headquarters in Kansas City was attributable to the Prime Time program. And the Republican Party became much more interested in bringing its national convention to the city in 1976 after working with Prime Time representatives. With this program, many new firms have been attracted to the area, resulting in several thousand new jobs. Prime Time is only one example of the way the Institute has reached helpfully into community life, but it is also a graphic representation of MRI's important role in economic studies and regional development planning.

In 1975, I retired as President of the Institute. The Trustees named as my successor John McKelvey, a Stanford M.B.A. who had come to MRI in 1964 as an economist and had worked his way through a succession of positions to Executive Vice President. Until 1979 when I was elected President Emeritus, I served as Chairman of the Board of Trustees.

The Institute continues to adapt, as it always has, to the changing interests of society, to the needs of sponsors, and to the fluctuating fortunes of research and development. Changes in the business climate and in government planning affect all organizations, and research institutes are no exception; indeed, they are perhaps more susceptible to the seismic shocks of such changes than many kinds of corporate endeavors. MRI has managed to adjust to the changes, still depending as always on the sponsored research that requires the Institute to sell its capabilities to sponsors over and over again, every year — since 95 percent of all research at the Institute is externally sponsored.

The future of research and development in almost every field is steadfastly unpredictable. Only a dozen years ago, 2 percent of MRI's research income came from studies on the environment, but by 1977, the figure had jumped to 40 percent. This dramatic shift illustrates how quickly the Institute must be ready to move in new directions with adequate staff and facilities to provide the required research.

An important element of the recent growth of MRI has been the U.S. Department of Energy's Solar Energy Research Institute (SERI) in Golden, Colorado. When John McKelvey became President of the Institute in May 1975, it was our best year to date — our research volume was more than $12 million and our staff numbered about 550 persons, of whom 385 were professionals. When in 1977 the Institute won a vigorous competition to serve as contractor/manager of SERI (against such giants in the field as Battelle, SRI International, and MIT, as well as Lockheed and Westinghouse), MRI began to expand rapidly, with staff and research volume more than doubling in three years. Early SERI efforts on analysis and applications of solar energy use were slowed when President Reagan's administration cut back solar energy funding in 1981 and SERI shifted toward long-range research in solar technology. In 1983, MRI won a five-year renewal of its contract with SERI, which remains the nation's premier solar research center.

Even oil-rich nations must look ahead to diminished supplies of this nonrenewable resource, and under joint sponsorship of the Kingdom of Saudi Arabia and the U.S. Department of Energy in Saudi Arabia, MRI is conducting a series of interrelated studies for that nation in applications of solar energy. Also of importance to the people of the Kingdom of Saudi Arabia is the development of a modern food inspection program for their country by MRI chemists, microbiologists, and food scientists. Another program, on land development studies, is under way for the King Faisal Foundation.

In addition to these major programs, there are about 150 other projects in the Institute at any given time, more than half of which are sponsored by private industry. However, about 75 percent of the dollar volume of projects — beyond SERI funding — comes from government projects. It is clear that the modern MRI has retained the concept of regional service and private industry sponsorship that the founders envisioned even as it has engaged in important international projects.

Yet, MRI's emphasis on quality research has never changed, although methods, materials, and demands have become more sophisticated. Certainly the Institute's national and international visibility is growing through projects such as SERI, but the same rigorous attention is still turned to the less visible, more modest locally sponsored projects that staff undertake.

In the beginning, marketing MRI's services was really a matter of letting the business and industrial community know how much we could help them; now marketing, too, has become sophisticated. To be successful in marketing, MRI experiments with diversification, in staff and in projects. The Institute tries to avoid dependence on any single market area and stresses having a balanced group of clients in different fields. It is particularly important that federal work be sponsored by different agencies and departments, and MRI has found a successful distribution.

The goals of the Institute today are growth in volume, quality research, improved business management, better marketing, and the infusion of new scientific talent — the same goals it had at the beginning, but now in expanded and differently focused forms. It is still a Midwestern institution, staffed in large measure by Midwesterners, and serving the needs of the Midwest as well as industries, agencies, and branches of government at local, state, and national levels — and beyond.

Today, the role of Midwest Research Institute is sometimes called an interface function. That is really only a contemporary term for the charge the Institute accepted at its founding: to bring the disciplines of science to bear on the needs of the overall community. Certainly that interface function has multiplied in the numbers and kinds of relationships it represents. Now, MRI can bring to any project — from local to international — a rich variety of resources. Multidisciplinary expertise, practical problem solving, independent status: these are the values the Institute has represented over the years as it has discovered more and more ways to relate the usefulness of inventions and processes to the environmental, societal, and personal needs of us all.

1965
·
1975

William C. Estler (above, right) of Palo Alto, California, and Leon T. Swan admire a Chesley Bonestell painting. MRI was given several works by Bonestell when he became interested in the Institute through the efforts of Bill Estler, who helped guide MRI's public relations efforts for nearly 25 years.

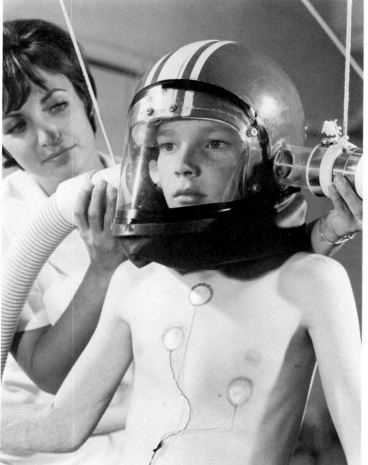

(left) A special assignment for MRI was the transfer of NASA's life science findings to the health care industry.

In the late 1960's and early 1970's, environmental pollution projects received increasing attention. Early pollution projects at MRI measured mercury levels in the Great Lakes in studies on fish contamination (facing page).

Regional economic development was the basis for many projects in the 1960's including the Kansas City International Airport, for which MRI created a comprehensive plan to monitor construction activities.

The Patterson Memorial Library (below, left), given to the Institute by the children of founder C.J. Patterson, houses significant collections in scientific fields.

Biologist Martin Schuler (below, right), at MRI since 1944, was one of the first technical employees of the Institute and is now Corporate Secretary. He was a main force behind Science Pioneers, formed by the *Kansas City Star*, MRI, and interested citizens to encourage young people in science through science fairs, lectures, and seminars. Science Pioneers has been the inspiration for dozens of similar organizations worldwide. The Greater Kansas City Science and Engineering Fair is the largest of its kind in the United States.

(left to right) Harold L. Stout, Director of Engineering; Dr. Warren E. Snyder; and Howard M. Gadberry discuss an experimental boiler constructed at the Deramus Field Station to evaluate boiler corrosion for the U.S. Navy in 1957.

The Deramus Field Station, a 45-acre farm on the outskirts of Kansas City, was donated to the Institute in 1957. Subsequent gifts by the Deramus family expanded to 78 acres the property now used for health sciences and for projects that require extensive outdoor space.

The Theis Room at MRI was a gift of W. C. Theis and Mary Louise Theis Kimball in 1969 in memory of their parents, Frank Albert and Rachel Coston Theis.

A new professional group of MRI's senior research staff was formed as the Council of Principal Scientists in 1972. Among the organizers were (above, from left) Larry Breed, Principal Chemist, and Jeff Maillie, Principal Economist.

Yudell Luke, head of applied mathematics at MRI and later University of Missouri-Kansas City Distinguished Professor of Mathematics.

The Barstow School loft, once an art studio, served many purposes for the Economics Division.

Social problems came into stronger focus in the 1960's and 1970's at MRI. One program was a national project for the Police Foundation to study crimes against the elderly and the need for protection in their homes.

An early device for measuring a driver's intoxication level, used in MRI's work on the Alcohol Safety Action Program (ASAP), a national program.

(below) In 1972, Dr. S. Johan Lundin (left) of the Stockholm International Peace Research Institute (SIPRI) came to discuss with R. E. Roberts of MRI approaches to limiting the production and stockpiling of chemical agents.

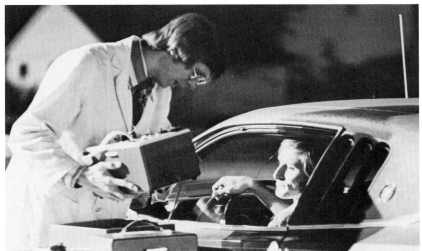

President Jimmy Carter with John McKelvey, President of MRI since 1975.

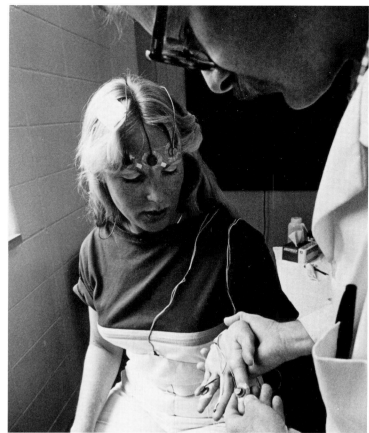

Psychophysiology research at MRI includes biofeedback studies which have been used in health care to relieve the pain of migraine and cancer, and to curb anorexia and various chemical addictions.

Presidents of the eight major not-for-profit research institutions in the United States met at MRI in 1971 to consider shared efforts in the scientific community.

A device to measure roadway air quality was developed by MRI as part of ongoing environmental studies. The device measures pollutants and fugitive dust at different levels above the road.

A specially developed inhalation chamber in the Kelce Memorial Laboratory (right) at the Deramus Field Station is used to evaluate toxic materials in the industrial workplace.

MRI employees with 20 or more years of service gathered for a photograph in 1984.

MRI was a three-time recipient of the prestigious I-R 100 awards given annually by *Industrial Research* magazine for the 100 most significant research developments. Here MRI staff members William Jacobs, Louis Goodson, and Francis Van Morriss are shown with Neil P. Ruzic, founder and publisher.

Linda Thornton, director of economics and social science, with Gene Vandegrift, discusses site planning with Trustee George P. Kroh, a Kansas City real estate developer.

A national Police Foundation project (left) studied the most appropriate crime-deterring techniques for specific urban areas.

Solar energy with its far-reaching implications for industry and for residences became increasingly important to MRI in the 1970's.

Duane N. Sunderman is Senior Vice President and Director, Kansas City Operations.

Dr. Harold M. Hubbard, named Director of Physical Sciences at MRI in 1970, is now Executive Vice President and Director of the Solar Energy Research Institute at Golden, Colorado, operated by MRI under contract for the U.S. Department of Energy.

John A. Dinwiddie, currently Senior Vice President and Chief Financial Officer of MRI, succeeded Leon T. Swan as Treasurer.

John C. McKelvey, a Stanford M.B.A. who had been with MRI since 1964, became President of the Institute in 1975.

MRI headquarters (below) today comprises 200,000 square feet of office, laboratory, and shop area. Specialized scientific equipment worth $8 million is housed in 125 laboratories.

(facing page) MRI is people: the Institute's most important discoveries were of the strengths and skills of its people.

TRUSTEES

A GATHERING OF FRIENDS

From the start, J. C. Nichols believed that great men should be associated with MRI because they would enable the Institute to be a powerful force within the mid-continent community. The role of trustees generally is to ensure that an organization remains fiscally responsible, but the role of MRI Trustees has always been much more.

One of the ways in which MRI is distinct from other research institutes is in its trustee relationships. The Institute has more Trustees, and they integrate the Institute more fully into the life of the local and regional community than is regularly the case with other institutes.

For example, Battelle Memorial Institute in Columbus, Ohio, the largest of the nation's research institutes, was founded as a result of a bequest by Gordon Battelle, a metallurgist. Its trustees, always a small group of about 10 members, come from various states, have a national outlook, and, until the last decade, have not been directly involved in regional or local affairs. Likewise, Southwest Research Institute in San Antonio, Texas, branched out from its early direction initially charted by founding president Harold Vagtborg, who came from MRI, and his successor, Martin Goland, who was at MRI from 1946 to 1955. Initially, Southwest was planned to have a regional focus of service much like MRI's, but for a variety of reasons took a national role and became a significant force in certain engineering and chemical technologies. Both Battelle and Southwest began with substantial financial backing.

Southern Research Institute of Birmingham, Alabama, was also very like MRI as it was founded, but it too developed differently. Begun by businessmen who hoped to stimulate the growth of the Deep South, Southern concentrated on cancer research, and its primary business became medical research rather than industrial investigation.

MRI, on the other hand, has kept the Midwestern focus it had at its founding, in part because the majority of its large 145-member Board of Trustees live in the metropolitan Kansas City area, or in nearby communities in Kansas and Missouri. Most of the remaining Trustees can easily commute to the Annual Meeting from within MRI's primary service area of Missouri, Kansas, Nebraska, Iowa, Arkansas, and Oklahoma. The president of Battelle, Sherwood Fawcett, said in 1975 that MRI was unique among all research institutes for its involvement of regional leadership.

MRI did not begin with a huge bequest or other large grant, and its financial stability over the years has been due in large part to the more than 800 contributors who have given sums ranging from $100 to $700,000. Approximately two-thirds of all gifts from all sources have come from Trustees as personal gifts, company contributions, foundation grants, or bequests. Of the gifts made exceeding $10,000, almost 90 percent have come from the Trustees. MRI Trustees, many of them heads of firms, have contributed more than $6 million since the first funding drive of the Institute in 1943. MRI's importance in the Kansas City community is evidenced by the fact that over 80 percent of all Trustee contributions have come from Trustees residing in the Greater Kansas City area.

Between 1943 and 1975, the net worth of the Institute had grown to nearly $10 million, including earnings that were put back into research and facilities and the value of the facilities and equipment made possible by contributions. Money was also given to MRI to set up three special funds — the Kimball Fund, the Mellon Fund, and the Battelle Fund.

In 1970, the Executive Committee of the Board of Trustees established the Kimball Fund to enable MRI to attack public problems that otherwise might not be undertaken; this fund also provides a means of investing in proposal or start-up projects that seem promising and that fit in with MRI's major programs. Much of the work to prepare the initial proposal for SERI was funded this way. The fund now stands at $1.5 million, the earnings of which are allocated by a special committee for public service and exploratory science projects. MRI staff have been active in Kansas City's economic development planning, and a number of planning studies have been funded through the Kimball Fund. Trustee contributions are thus recycled through the community.

The Mellon Fund began as a grant of $500,000, a gift in 1964 from Richard King Mellon of Pittsburgh, made in recognition of MRI's achievements. The income from the Mellon Fund has occasionally been used to retain valuable staff during transitions between projects.

The Battelle Fund, established in 1970, is remarkable because it involved one research institute putting a portion of its endowment at the disposal of another. With this formal recognition of MRI, Battelle's faith in intensive regional development through science and technology has led to significant initiatives within MRI.

Money-raising activities are only one aspect of the contributions of MRI Trustees. Over the years when MRI was becoming established, I described Trustee involvement as "advocacy." Probably a fifth of my time as President was spent working with Trustees to encourage an active interest in MRI, not just through their donations but through project referrals as well. In one five-year period during the 1960's, more than 40 percent of the private sector projects coming to MRI were from Trustee involvement, either as direct research sponsored by companies they managed or as Trustee referrals to other firms. Civic committees in Kansas City almost always include MRI Trustees, and in many cases these people call upon MRI for help in backup research and proposal preparation. For example, in 1975 when the Chamber of Commerce commissioned a committee to plan ways in which the city could continue expansion of its economic base, MRI staff produced the report and prepared plans for implementation.

In the beginning, MRI had two groups of governing bodies: a Board of Governors and the Board of Trustees. The Board of Governors met monthly to approve changes in staff, policy, and budget, while the full Board of Trustees met once or twice a year. This arrangement was revised in 1960 to create a single Board of Trustees with an Executive Committee.

The Executive Committee consisted mostly of local members who met on a regular basis, usually monthly. The full Board of Trustees, on which persons of regional and national prominence are asked to serve, has for years visited the Institute once a year, during the week of the Annual Meeting held in Kansas City each May. Currently, there is also an interim meeting held in December.

The Annual Meeting is the primary public relations effort of the year. Given the importance of Trustee advocacy, this annual session provides the main forum for the Institute's leadership to inform Trustees of MRI's current activities and interests.

Coinciding with the Annual Meeting is the presentation of the Annual Trustees' Citation, a tradition now in its 27th year. Distinguished individuals are invited to receive the Citation and to present an address which is then reprinted and sent to a select group of business and community leaders throughout the Midwest and beyond. Although most of the honorees have been selected because their careers show an awareness of the importance of science and technology to American culture, their addresses have touched on a wide range of topics. MRI is the only research institute to hold a major annual meeting of this kind, and to present such an award.

For many years, the Trustees of MRI were far better known than the Institute itself, but founder J. C. Nichols' notion of attracting great men to the service of MRI has proved sound, and the Institute has come to deserve the confidence of these leaders. Many of the Institute's Trustees have participated in MRI's Midcontinent Perspectives Series, which annually since 1974 has presented six lectures on subjects of regional and national concern. Monographs of each address and the question-and-answer period that follows are printed and distributed to several thousand persons nationwide. Of the first 28 presentations, 25 were delivered by Trustees.

The years during which MRI came into its own as a vital, influential force in the community of science and in the region it serves were marked by the vision and contributions of Trustees. The Trustees have guaranteed that MRI has had the facilities to compete in the research field. As contributors of money and project referrals, as providers of market or technology intelligence, and as sounding boards for new ideas, the Trustees have been important to every phase of MRI's growth. Indeed, the Board of Trustees has been more than a prestigious symbol of Institute operations; it has been a gathering of friends of the Institute.

Trustees at the 1977 Annual Meeting gather outside the Arthur Mag Conference Center, used for MRI conferences and board and staff meetings and seminars, and by many civic and philanthropic organizations. The center was financed by a major gift of the Stinson, Mag & Fizzell Foundation in honor of Mr. Mag, and by gifts from many of his friends throughout the region.

James M. Kemper, Sr., Miller Nichols, Arthur Mag, and W. N. Deramus, Sr., at MRI Annual Meeting in 1949.

Michael E. DeBakey, M.D., Baylor University College of Medicine, recipient of the MRI Citation in 1966, visits with W.N. Deramus III, Chairman of Trustees, 1966-1968.

101

(top, left) Trustee James A. Alcott, an MRI staff member from 1958 to 1969, now Vice President-Administration, Cowles Media Company.

(top, right) Trustee Dolph C. Simons, Jr., editor and publisher, *The Lawrence Daily Journal-World*.

(center, left) John B. Gage (left), Vice Chairman of Trustees, 1949-1956, with Byron T. Shutz, a Trustee from 1947 to 1980.

(center, right) Oklahoma publisher E. K. Gaylord, a Trustee from 1944 until his death in 1974, was the recipient of the MRI Citation in 1958.

(right) Edward Teller (left), director of the Lawrence Radiation Laboratory and MRI Citation recipient in 1960, and Marvin B. Marsh, Chairman of Trustees, 1960-1962, at the 1960 Annual Meeting.

Trustee Dr. Robert R. Wheeler discussed "Public Education in the Year 2000" at the Annual Meeting in 1978.

(right) John H. Kreamer (left), Chairman of Trustees, 1984-1986, with David H. Hughes, Vice Chairman, 1984-1986.

(below, right) George E. Powell, Jr. (left), Chairman of Trustees, 1968-1970, with Trustee R. M. Patterson, chairman of the board, C. J. Patterson Company.

(below, left) Trustee Ben D. McCallister, M.D. (left), with W. G. Shepherd, chairman of the advisory board of North Star Research Institute.

(above, left) Morton I. Sosland, Chairman of Trustees, 1974-1976.

Joyce C. Hall (above, right), the chairman of the board of Hallmark Cards, Inc., received the MRI Citation in 1972.

(left) Trustee Charles W. Battey (left), Chairman of Trustees, 1982-1984, with Robert A. Long, Chairman of Trustees, 1980-1982.

John A. Morgan, Chairman of Trustees, 1964-1966.

(above, left) Franklin D. Murphy, former Chancellor of the University of Kansas and recipient of the MRI Citation in 1970.

(above, right) Richard King Mellon, chairman of the board, Mellon National Bank and Trust Company, was the MRI Citation recipient in 1964.

Irvine O. Hockaday, Jr. (left), Chairman of Trustees, 1978-1980, and Walter Cronkite, recipient of the MRI Citation in 1979.

W.C. Theis (left), Vice Chairman of Trustees, and Donald Hall, Chairman of Trustees, 1976-1978.

(above, right) Trustee Ilus W. Davis, mayor of Kansas City, 1963-1971.

Trustee D. A. McGee (left), chairman of the board of Kerr-McGee Corporation and recipient of the MRI Citation in 1973, with Dr. Sherwood Fawcett, president of Battelle Memorial Institute.

George C. Dillon, chairman of the board, Butler Manufacturing Company, addresses the Annual Meeting as Chairman of Trustees in 1970.

Trustee Willis A. Strauss (left), chairman of the board, InterNorth, Inc., with Paul H. Henson, chairman, United Telecommunications, Inc., at the 1976 Annual Meeting.

(corner) Arthur Mag (left), Chairman of Trustees, 1958-1960, with Roy W. Menninger, M.D., Vice Chairman of Trustees, 1981-1982.

(right) Robert H. Gaynor (left), Chairman of Trustees, 1972-1974, presented the MRI Citation in 1974 to John D. deButts, chairman of the board of American Telephone & Telegraph.

(below) Trustees George C. Dillon (right) and Rev. M. E. Van Ackeren, S.J. (left), visit with Joseph C. Shipman, director of the Linda Hall Library at an Annual Meeting.

(corner) John W. Gardner, president, Carnegie Corporation, received the MRI Citation in 1965.

(above) Trustees Senator Stuart Symington (D-Mo.) (left) and Donald J. Hall, chairman of the board, Hallmark Cards, Inc., at the 1979 Trustees meeting.

(left) Charles C. Tillinghast, Jr., president, Trans World Airlines, MRI Citation recipient in 1967.

A thousand people sat down to dinner at MRI's Annual Meeting in 1975.

EPILOGUE

Even an amateur historian feels the relief of being able to leave history still actively in the making. Charting MRI's first 30 years of discovery relives for me the vigor, challenge, and excitement of seeing such an institution come into its own. I believe that whoever sets down MRI's next 30 years will have a task as rewarding, just differently focused.

Over the years, MRI has earned cherished status, day by day, year by year, through being predictable and reliable in its research and outreach. For many individuals, companies, and institutions, MRI serves as a "trusted source." It has maintained an integrity of purpose governed by its charter, while at the same time it has been flexible enough to accommodate the explosion of change in both science and industry.

That integrity of purpose was recognized in 1983 by a Federal court in an unprecedented ruling that allowed MRI to recover over a half-million dollars in back taxes, paid under protest for income from projects undertaken for private sponsors during the 1961 and 1970 periods.

Despite MRI's initially having been granted tax-exempt status in 1947, the IRS had come over the years to contend that the privately sponsored work performed by the Institute was not necessarily in the public interest and did not fall within the purpose for which MRI received its tax-exempt status in the first place. With the assistance of MRI's long-time tax advisor, Reece A. Gardner, we argued that MRI's charter called for assisting the retention of business in the region and attracting new enterprise through scientific research. For 25 years the controversy carried on until the IRS and MRI had no alternative but to settle the issue in court. MRI paid the assessed taxes and filed a refund suit in the United States District Court in 1977.

It was the first such suit to be brought by a research organization and the verdict was historic. U.S. District Court Judge Howard F. Sachs ruled that most projects undertaken for private sponsors were indeed substantially related to MRI's tax-exempt purpose of providing scientific research necessary to the industrial and economic development of the Midwest.

In 1984, a Federal Court of Appeals upheld Judge Sachs' ruling in a decision that reaffirmed the significance of MRI's purpose as defined by its charter. By holding to its original charge despite its growth and changes, MRI has won respect for the integrity of the Board and of the professional management and staff.

An unfailing regard for MRI's main purpose can be measured in the exemplary way in which Trustees have answered the management's call for help, whether for capital funds, new buildings, new ventures, or new contacts. MRI has truly become an "institution" in the life of the Midwest, and such a vital element of this part of the country that it is hard to imagine its not being here.

For me, the connection between the Institute and the broad midcontinent community has always been inseparable, and I hope it continues that way. To paraphrase Samuel Johnson's remark about the maintenance of human relationships, "An institution should keep its friendships in good repair."

I've tried to set down in this record some of the experiences of the first 30 years, in prose and in pictures. From this perspective, it is clear that MRI's most important discoveries were of the strengths and skills of its people. Their motivations were high and consistent. They were usually creative crusaders, more interested in client outcomes than in their own well-being, physical or financial. Through them the dreams of the founders were bettered.

MRI's people were creative and diligent. I like a definition of "creative effort" I once read: "The imagination that looks forward, foresees, supplies, competes, plans, invents, solves, advances, and originates." There isn't a single passive verb in the list. But our people add one more dimension to creative effort. That is closure ability, the capacity to bring something to a definite conclusion and not keep researching it to death. In research, knowing when to quit a project is sometimes more difficult than knowing when to start one.

The spirit of the Institute was, with rare exceptions, first rate. There was little bureaucracy and much help provided by one person to another.

Dr. Lee DuBridge, who was probably as respected a spokesman for science as there was in the free world, said shortly after World War II, "There really have not been very many spectacularly productive research organizations, either civilian or military. Whenever you find a highly successful group, I suggest you seek the causes for its success not in the organizational chart, not in the budget, not by counting uniforms or rank, not by the splendor of its buildings or equipment, but that you look around and find. . .a small group of men who have created the spirit of that place and who know how to preserve that spirit."

Somehow or other that kind of a small group has always appeared at MRI when it was most needed. In the early years, I suspect it was Max Thornton, Leon Swan, and myself. Now, in the years since 1975, it is John McKelvey, Harold Hubbard, Jack Dinwiddie, and, more recently, Duane Sunderman, with their selected management group.

I believe that others like them are here among the present staff and will emerge as the future demands their contributions to the ongoing spirit of MRI. To make a place like this go takes individual skill and institutional willpower. It takes an ability to integrate science and technology into the rest of the world.

Forty years ago MRI was trying to develop into an institute that would, first of all, find economic and professional stability, define its true mission, and then meet the region's needs for research support as those developed. Now, as a mature organization, we are also seeking ways to work on problems and opportunities measured by world needs and influence.

MRI's ability to adapt to changes and to discover new directions comes in large part from its status as an independent and freestanding institution, not bound in its scope to any permanent affiliation with a government, organization, or university. We have not been restricted so far by geography, nor by any external forces beyond those of the marketplace.

Hence, we've been quite free to take the longer view, to anticipate many issues before they arise.

Still, MRI's home and heart are in this region. And the Midwest is no longer the nation's backwater. It is the new hope for the world's appetite for food, goods, and gifted people with broad and generous outlooks. MRI still has a major part to play in helping determine the Midwest's pattern of survival and orderly growth.

This Midwestern community has been good to MRI and to its people. I sometimes have thought, where else could a guy have come in some 35 years ago, almost a total stranger, and have been given the help and the acceptance I've had? I doubt very much that it could have happened in Baltimore, Boston, Detroit, New York, or San Francisco. The kind of willing help I found here came to the Institute as a whole, and remains in the history of MRI as a debt that only continuing competence in research and extended outreach can repay.

Nonetheless, as deep as the debt to the community may be, I expect that it will be repaid by this remarkable institution. I expect that this "lighthouse on the prairie" will continue to illuminate many of the issues that confront the Midwest region, the nation, and, indeed, the world. If we summed up all our discoveries of the first 30 years in one description of Midwest Research Institute, it would surely be our shared sense of wonder and eagerness at all there is yet to discover.

BOARD OF GOVERNORS

	Chairman	Vice Chairman
1958 - 1960	Arthur Mag	Miller Nichols
1956 - 1958	A.R. Waters	Miller Nichols
1954 - 1956	Harry Moreland	Miller Nichols
1951 - 1954	Kenneth A. Spencer	Louis S. Rothschild
1949 - 1951	C.J. Patterson	Kenneth A. Spencer
1948	J.F. Stephens	
1947	R.L. Mehornay	T.J. Strickler
1944 - 1946	R.L. Mehornay	